Grade **1**

Scott Foresman

Texas

Reader's and Writer's Notebook

D1377347

 PEARSON Glenview, Illinois • Boston, Massachusetts • Chandler, Arizona •
Upper Saddle River, New Jersey

The Texas Essential Knowledge and Skills for English Language Arts and Reading reproduced by permission, Texas Education Agency, 1701 N. Congress Avenue, Austin, TX 78701

ISBN 13: 978-0-328-49578-8
ISBN 10: 0-328-49578-6
9 10 11 12 V011 19 18 17 16

Readiness: My World

Contents

Unit 1: Animals, Tame and Wild

Unit 2: Communities

Unit 3: Changes

Unit 4: Treasures

© Pearson Education, Inc., 1

Contents

Unit 5: Great Ideas

Name _____

Unit R Reading Log

Reading Time	Title and Author	What is it about?	How would you rate it?	Why?
From ____ to ____			Great OK Awful	
From ____ to ____			Great OK Awful	
From ____ to ____			Great OK Awful	
From ____ to ____			Great OK Awful	
From ____ to ____			Great OK Awful	

1.12.A.1 Read independently for a sustained period of time.

Name _____

Unit 1 Reading Log

Reading Time	Title and Author	What is it about?	How would you rate it?	Why?
From ___ to ___			Great OK Awful	
From ___ to ___			Great OK Awful	
From ___ to ___			Great OK Awful	
From ___ to ___			Great OK Awful	
From ___ to ___			Great OK Awful	
From ___ to ___			Great OK Awful	

1.12.A.1 Read independently for a sustained period of time.

Name _____

Unit 2 Reading Log

Reading Time	Title and Author	What is it about?	How would you rate it?	Why?
From ____ to ____			Great OK Awful	
From ____ to ____			Great OK Awful	
From ____ to ____			Great OK Awful	
From ____ to ____			Great OK Awful	
From ____ to ____			Great OK Awful	
From ____ to ____			Great OK Awful	

1.12.A.1 Read independently for a sustained period of time.

Independent Reading   RR3

Name _____

Unit 3 Reading Log

Reading Time	Title and Author	What is it about?	How would you rate it?	Why?
From ____ to ____			Great OK Awful	
From ____ to ____			Great OK Awful	
From ____ to ____			Great OK Awful	
From ____ to ____			Great OK Awful	
From ____ to ____			Great OK Awful	
From ____ to ____			Great OK Awful	

RR4 **Independent Reading**

1.12.A.1 Read independently for a sustained period of time.

Name _____

Unit 4 Reading Log

Reading Time	Title and Author	What is it about?	How would you rate it?	Why?
From ____ to ____			Great OK Awful	
From ____ to ____			Great OK Awful	
From ____ to ____			Great OK Awful	
From ____ to ____			Great OK Awful	
From ____ to ____			Great OK Awful	
From ____ to ____			Great OK Awful	

🟊 **1.12.A.1** Read independently for a sustained period of time.

Name _____

Unit 5 Reading Log

Reading Time	Title and Author	What is it about?	How would you rate it?	Why?
From ____ to ____			Great OK Awful	
From ____ to ____			Great OK Awful	
From ____ to ____			Great OK Awful	
From ____ to ____			Great OK Awful	
From ____ to ____			Great OK Awful	
From ____ to ____			Great OK Awful	

1.12.A.1 Read independently for a sustained period of time.

Name _Miko_

Story Title _____

Author _____

> A **picture walk** can help you learn about a story.

Look at the pictures in the story. What do you want to find out about the story?

Draw a picture of the thing or person you have a question about.

Who is the character in the story? **How** does the character feel or act? **Write**.

_____

_____

_____

_____

Name _____

Story Title _____

Author _____

> You can look at the pictures in a story and **predict** what might happen in the story.
>
> You can **set a purpose** for reading by thinking about why you want to read this story.

Look at the pictures in the story.
What do you predict about the story?
Draw a picture about your prediction. **Write** a label about it.

Check your predictions. **Read** the part that tells in the story.
Write where the story takes place.

_____

- -

_____

1.4.A.1 Confirm predictions about what will happen next in text by "reading the part that tells." **Also 1.4.C.1, 1.9, RC-1.A.1.**

Name _____

Story Title _____

Author _____

Circle the sentences that are true about realistic fiction.

It has animals that talk like people.

There are characters.

It has a setting.

It tells about things that could really happen.

_____

Draw pictures to show what happens at the beginning, the middle, and end of the story.

1.9 Understand the structure and elements of fiction.

Name _____

Story Title _____

Author _____

> You can **ask questions** about what you are going to read to better understand the story.

Look at the pictures in the story. What **questions** would you like to ask about the characters and events in the story? **Write**.

_____
_____
_____
_____
_____
_____
_____

Circle each sentence that tells about realistic fiction.

It is a made up story that could happen in real life.

It is a story that could not happen.

There are one or more characters in the story.

It has a beginning, middle, and end.

© Pearson Education, Inc., 1

1.4.B.1 Ask relevant questions about stories. **Also 1.4.B.2, 1.9,** RC-1.C.1.

Name _____

Story Title _____

Author _____

Look at the pictures of the story. **Think** about what you know about the topic. **Write** a question about the story.

_____
_____
_____
_____

After reading, **reread** the part of the story that answers your question. Did you have to make any corrections to your question?

What happened in the story? **Draw** the problem or the solution.

Name _____

Story Title _____

Author _____

What do you think the characters in the story will see at the farmers market? **Draw** pictures and **write** labels.

```




```

Write a sentence in each box telling what happened in the story.

Beginning

⬇

Middle

⬇

End

RC-1.F.1 Comprehend a variety of texts drawing on useful strategies as needed. **Also RC-1.F.2, 1.9.**

Name _____

Story Title _____

Author _____

> When you read, you should understand what and why things happen in the story.
>
> **Ask questions** about the story before you read and then look for the answers in the story.

What would you do if you read a part of a story that did not make sense to you? **Write**.

_____
- -
_____
_____
- -
_____

Think about the story you just read. **Write** or **draw** what you did to understand the events in the story.

1.4.C.2 Monitor comprehension, making corrections when the understanding breaks down. **Also 1.4.C.3.**

Name _____

Story Title _____

Author _____

> A story can be a **fantasy**. This kind of story is made up.

Look at the pictures of the story. How do you know this is a fantasy? **Write**.

_____
- -
_____
- -
_____

> When you summarize a story, you tell the most important parts of the story in your own words.

Draw a picture to tell about an important event in the story.

RC-1-D.1 Make inferences about text. **Also RC-1-D.2, 1.9.**

© Pearson Education, Inc. 1

Name _____

Story Title _____

Author _____

Think about what you know about an ox. **Draw** a picture about how an ox can help on a farm. Write a sentence to tell about your picture.

When you **visualize** a story, you form pictures in your mind based on the details from the story.

RC-1-D.1 Make inferences about text.   **Also RC-1-D.2, 1.9.**

Name _____

Story Title _____

Author _____

Draw a picture of a fox and a kit.

_____

Draw a picture of what you think was the most important event in the story.

1.14.A.1 Restate the main idea, read. **Also 1.4, RC-1.C.1, 1.4.B.7.**

© Pearson Education, Inc. 1

Name _____

Story Title _____

Author _____

Look at the cover and the title of the story. Where do you think the story takes place? **Draw** the setting. **Explain** your drawing.

Think about the beginning, middle and end of the story. **Draw** a picture of the most important event in the story. Include the characters and setting of the story.

Name _____

Story Title _____

Author _____

Underline the sentences that tell about literary nonfiction.

It tells information about real characters or places.

The characters are always animals.

It is a made up story.

It gives information about an event.

The events of the story happened in a certain order. **Draw** a picture of what the author saw at the animal park right after she saw the zebras. **Write** a label.

1.10 Understand, make inferences, and draw conclusions about the varied structural patterns and features of literary nonfiction. **Also 1.14.D.1.**

Name _____

Story Title _____

Author _____

Tell what you know about animal families. Then **look** at the pictures in the story. Predict what the story will be about and what might happen. **Write**.

_____
_____
_____
_____
_____
_____

Check your predictions. **Read** the part that tells in the story. Were your predictions correct? What was surprising and why? **Write**.

_____
_____
_____
_____
_____
_____
_____
_____
_____
_____

Name _____

Story Title _____

Author _____

> When you read, you should understand what and why things happen in the story.
>
> **Ask questions** about the story before you read and then look for clues in the story.

Write some questions about the story to help you better understand the story when you read.

_____
_____
_____
_____
_____
_____
_____

Look at the story again. What part did you not understand?
Write what you did to understand that part of the story.

_____
_____
_____
_____
_____
_____
_____

1.4.C.3 Monitor comprehension, making adjustments when the understanding breaks down. **Also 1.4.C.2, 1.4.B.2.**

Name _____

Story Title _____

Author _____

Underline the sentences that tell about expository text.

It is a made up story.

It gives facts and details.

It can be about real people, animals or places.

It is a story that should be acted out.

Write three facts you learned from reading the selection.

_____
_____
_____
_____
_____
_____
_____
_____
_____
_____
_____
_____

1.10 Understand, make inferences, and draw conclusions about
the varied structural patterns and features of literary nonfiction.
Also 1.14.D.1.

Name _____

Story Title _____

Author _____

What do you know about dinosaurs? **Write** about when and how dinosaurs lived.

_____
- -
_____
_____
- -
_____
_____
- -
_____

Think about **what you knew** about dinosaurs before you read the story. Then use what you know and the clues in the text to **tell more** about dinosaurs. **Write** a list.

RC-1.D.1 Make inferences about text. **Also RC-1.D.2, 1.4, 1.4.B.8.**

Name _____

Story Title _____

Author _____

Draw a picture of an animal that lives in a forest.
Write a sentence about your picture.

_____

- -

_____

Now **draw** your favorite forest animal. Tell the most important
things about the animal. **Write** a caption.

_____

- -

_____

Name _____

Story Title _____

Author _____

> You can **ask questions** about what you are going to read to better understand the story.

Look at the pictures in the text. What questions would you like to ask? **Write**.

_____
_____
_____
_____
_____
_____
_____

Look for the answers to your questions in the text. **Write** the answers.

_____
_____
_____
_____
_____
_____
_____
_____

RC-1.B.1 Ask literal questions of text. **Also** 1.4.B.1, 1.4.B.2, 1.4.B.5, 1.4.B.6.

Name _____

Story Title _____

Author _____

Draw a picture of your favorite place to play.
Why is this your favorite place? **Write** a sentence.

```




```

- -

- -

Look at the picture you drew. **How** would you change it?
Add to your picture to show what you would change.

```




```

Name _____

Story Title _____

Author _____

Circle the sentences that are true about an animal fantasy.

The characters are animals.

It is a story that could happen in real life.

The animals can talk.

The animals act like people.

Think about **what you knew** about animals before you read the story. **Draw** pictures to show the things you knew that helped you better understand the story.

RC-1-D.1 Make inferences about text. **Also RC-1-D.2, 1.9.**

Name _____

Story Title _____

Author _____

Underline each sentence that is true about **expository text.**

It gives facts and details.

It tells about real people or animals.

The story may tell how make-believe characters act.

It is a play.

Think about something in the story that was hard to understand.
Write what you did to understand this part of the story.

_____
_____
_____
_____
_____
_____
_____
_____
_____
_____
_____

RC-1.C.1 Monitor comprehension. **Also RC-1.C.2, 1.9.**

Name _____

Story Title _____

Author _____

Draw a picture of a seed and a flower.
What can a gardener do to help the seed become a flower?
Write a sentence.

[ ]

_____

- - - - - - - - - - - - - - - - - - - -

_____

Draw a picture of Toad in his garden once it has bloomed.
How does Toad feel about his garden? **Write** a sentence.

[ ]

_____

- - - - - - - - - - - - - - - - - - - -

_____

1.11.A.1 Recognize sensory details in literary text.
Also RC-1.C.1.

Name _____

Story Title _____

Author _____

Circle the sentences that are true about literary nonfiction.

It teaches a lesson.

It describes events that happen in real life.

It gives information about real people or animals.

It tells about make-believe things.

Draw pictures of three things that happen in the life cycle of a butterfly. **Write** the number 1, 2, or 3 under each picture to show the order of the events.

_____   _____   _____

- - - - - - - - -   - - - - - - - - -   - - - - - - - - -

_____   _____   _____

Name _____

Story Title _____

Author _____

Draw a picture of an animal getting ready for winter.
Write a label for the animal.
Then **write** a sentence telling what the animal is doing.

_____

_____

_____

_____

How is a play different from a story? **Write**.

_____

_____

_____

_____

_____

RC-1.F.1 Comprehend a variety of texts drawing on useful
strategies as needed.   **Also 1.4.**

Name _____

Story Title _____

Author _____

What if something in the story you are about to read doesn't make sense?

Draw a picture of what you will do. **Write** a sentence about it.

┌─────────────────────────────────┐
│   │
│   │
│   │
│   │
│   │
│   │
│   │
└─────────────────────────────────┘

_____
- - - - - - - - - - - - - - - - - -
_____

Think about parts of the story that didn't make sense to you.
Draw what you did to help you understand what was happening.
Write a sentence about it.

┌─────────────────────────────────┐
│   │
│   │
│   │
│   │
│   │
│   │
│   │
│   │
└─────────────────────────────────┘

_____
- - - - - - - - - - - - - - - - - -

RC-1.C.1 Monitor comprehension.   Also RC-1.C.2, 1.4.C.2, 1.4.C.3.

Name _____

Story Title _____

Author _____

Circle the sentences that are true about a fairy tale.

The characters are often princes or princesses.

The story takes place long ago.

The story tells information about real events.

The setting is in a make-believe land.

When you **visualize** a story, you form pictures in your mind based on the details from the story.

Draw a picture of Cinderella's dress or her coach. Write a label.

1.11.A.1 Recognize sensory details in literary text.
Also RC-1.C.1.

Name _____

Story Title _____

Author _____

Draw a picture of a place you have visited on a trip.
Write a sentence about the thing you liked best about the place.

_____

_____

What did you learn from the story? **Write** two or three facts.

_____

_____

_____

_____

_____

_____

1.4.B.7 Locate facts about other texts.   **Also 1.4.B.8.**

Name _____

Story Title _____

Author _____

What questions do you have about life on a ranch?
Write your questions.

_____
_____
_____
_____
_____
_____
_____

When you read, you should look for answers to your
questions. Remember that sometimes a story will not
answer every question.

Look at the questions you wrote before reading the story.
Write answers to as many questions as you can.

_____
_____
_____
_____
_____
_____
_____

1.4.B.5 Ask relevant questions about other texts.
Also 1.4.B.1, 1.4.B.2, 1.4.B.6, RC-1.B.1.

Name _____

Story Title _____

Author _____

Draw a picture of your favorite thing from when you were a baby. **Why** was it your favorite? **Write** a sentence.

A **fiction story** has three parts. It has a beginning, a middle, and an end.

Think about the story you just read. **How** did knowing about the parts of a story help you understand what was happening? **Write** sentences to explain.

_____

_____

_____

_____

1.9 Understand the structure and elements of fiction.
Also 1.4.

Name _____

Story Title _____

Author _____

Look at the pictures in the story.
Write what you predict will happen in the story.

_____

_____

_____

_____

Think about why you want to read this story.
Write a purpose for reading it.

_____

_____

_____

_____

Check your prediction. **Read** the part in the story that tells
what did happen.
Write a sentence telling if your prediction was correct or not.

_____

_____

_____

_____

1.4.A.1 Confirm predictions about what will happen next in text
by "reading the part that tells."   **Also 1.4.C.1, RC-1.A.1.**

Name _____

Story Title _____

Author _____

> When you read, you should understand what and why things happen in the story. **Look for clues** in the pictures before you read and then read to find out what the clues mean.

What will you do if you don't understand what you read?
Write a sentence.

_____
- -
_____
_____
- -
_____

You wrote what you would do if you didn't understand part of a story. **Reread** what you wrote above. If you did this, **write** how it helped you. If you did something else, **write** how that helped you.

_____
- -
_____
_____
- -
_____
_____
- -
_____
_____
- -
_____

1.4.B.2 Seek clarification about stories. **Also** 1.4.B.3, 1.4.B.4, 1.4.C.2, 1.4.C.3, RC-1.C.1.

Name _____

Story Title _____

Author _____

Draw pictures of people taking care of their pets. How do you think the pets feel about their owners? **Write** a sentence.

When you **summarize** a story, you tell the most important parts of the story in your own words.

Summarize the story you just read. **Write** two or three sentences.

1.4 Comprehend a variety of texts drawing on useful strategies as needed. **Also RC-1.F.1.**

Name _____

Story Title _____

Author _____

What is informational fiction? **Write.**

_____

_____

_____

_____

_____

_____

Did you find parts of the story that were hard to understand?
Write what you used or would use to better understand the story.

_____

_____

_____

_____

_____

_____

1.4.C.2 Monitor comprehension, making corrections when that
understanding breaks down. **Also 1.4.C.3, RC-1.C.1, RC-1.C.2.**

Name _____

Story Title _____

Author _____

Tell about machines that you have seen.
Where did you see those machines?
What jobs do they do? Then draw a picture
of a machine you use often.

```
┌─────────────────────────────────────────┐
│                                         │
│                                         │
│                                         │
│                                         │
│                                         │
│                                         │
│                                         │
└─────────────────────────────────────────┘
```

Summarize the story you just read. **Write** three sentences.

_____
_____
_____
_____
_____
_____

RC-1.D.1 Make inferences about text.   **Also RC-1.D.2.**

Name _____

Story Title _____

Author _____

What is a biography? **Circle** the words that make the sentences true.

A biography is a _____ story.   made-up   true

A biography gives _____ about a person's life.   facts   jokes

A biography tells about a _____ person.   magic   real

You can think about how a **text is organized** to better understand what you are reading. Sequence is one way a text can be organized.

Write three events from Alexander Graham Bell's life. **Write** the events in the order in which they happened.

_____

_____

_____

_____

_____

_____

_____

_____

Name _____

Story Title _____

Author _____

Think about what you know about gardens.
What are some things that grow in gardens?
Write sentences to tell what you know.

_____
_____
_____
_____
_____
_____
_____
_____

Write what you learned about how people help their communities by reading this story.

_____
_____
_____
_____
_____
_____
_____
_____

🌀 **RC-1.D.1** Make inferences about text. **Also RC-1.D.2.**

Name _____

Book Talk Tips

- Talk about a book you like.

- Use a loud, clear voice.

- Look at your classmates.

- Don't tell how it ends!

Directions   When you talk about a book, answer these questions.

1. What is the title of the book?

2. Who is the author?

3. What kind of book is it?

4. What other book has the author written?

5. Tell what you liked the best.

6. Tell why they should read the book.

1.13.A.1 Identify the topic of the text.   **Independent Reading   RR43**

Name _____

Before Writing

- Think about ideas with a friend.

- Ask questions to help your friend pick a good topic.

Tips for Conferencing

- Read your friend's paper out loud. Listen for what you like.

- Tell your friend three things you like. Say: "I like how you ____."

- Read your friend's paper out loud again. Listen for what you do not understand.

- Ask your friend two questions that you have.

It might help to think about the:

- Title

- Beginning

- Ending

- Words that were used

- Use of verbs, nouns, adjectives or adverbs

1.17.E.2 Share writing with others.

Name _____

Title of Writing _____

Directions   Answer these questions about what you wrote.

1. What are the two things that are best about this?

_____

- -

_____

- -

_____

2. What is one thing you could have done better?

_____

- -

_____

3. Do you like what you wrote? Why or why not?

_____

- -

_____

- -

_____

Name _____

Mm

Say the word for each picture.
Write m on the line if the word has the same first sound as .

1. M m

2. A a

3. H h

4. M m

5. R r

6. G g

7. F f

8. M m

School + Home

Home Activity Your child has reviewed words that start with *m*. Help your child think of other words with
/m/ as in *map*.

1.2.E.1 Isolate initial sounds in one-syllable spoken words. **Also 1.2.E.3, 1.3.A.2.i.12.**

Phonics Consonant *Mm*/m/   **1**

Name _____

Draw your favorite character from a story you know.
Tell what the character is doing.
Tell how the character feels.

Home Activity Your child learned that characters in a story can be people or animals. As you read together, have your child tell you what he or she knows about the characters in stories.

2   Comprehension Character   ⊛**1.9.B.1** Describe characters in a story. **Also 1.9.B.2, 1.9.B.3.**

Name _____

Trace and **write** the letters. Make sure you write your letters the correct size.

Home Activity Your child practiced writing *M* and *m*. Say names and words that begin with *M* and *m* and have your child write the correct letter each time you say a name or word.

1.21.A.1 Form upper-case letters legibly in text, using the basic conventions of print (left-to-right and top-to-bottom progression), including spacing between words and sentences. **Also 1.1.B.1, 1.1.B.2, 1.21.A.2.**

Handwriting 3

Name _____

Circle the group that could be a real word.

1. (mat)　　　p2n　　　123　　　s3m　　　546

2. 237　　　e8b　　　476　　　ti9　　　(pan)

3. 530　　　213　　　63b　　　(Sam)　　　pp2

4. 760　　　(tap)　　　m22　　　310　　　614

Look at the first group of letters. **Circle** the group of letters that is in the same order as the first group.

5. pan　　　(pan)　　　nap　　　pna

6. cap　　　　　　tap　　　(cap)　　　pta

7. mat　　　　　　map　　　abt　　　(mat)

8. bag　　　　　　bad　　　(bag)　　　dma

Home Activity Your child identified groups of letters and compared the sequence of letters in words or letter groups such as *pan, nap,* and *pna.* Write some groups of numbers and some words. Have your child pick out the words.

4   Print Awareness

1.1.A 1. Recognize that spoken words are represented in written English by specific sequences of letters.

Name _____

Ss

Say the word for each picture.
Write s on the line if the word has the same first sound as .

1. sandwich	_S s_	2. seesaw	_S s_
3. socks	_S s_	4. motorcycle	_M m_
5. hat	_H h_	6. sun	_S s_
7. map	_M m_	8. submarine	_S s_

Phonics Consonant _Ss_/s/ **5**

Nouns: People, Animals, and Things

A **noun** names a person, an animal, or a thing.

The word **boy** names a person.

The word **cat** names an animal.

The word **bed** names a thing.

Circle the correct noun for each picture.
Say a sentence for each noun.

boy   girl

car   bus

pig   dog

mom   dad

Home Activity Your child learned about nouns that name people or things. Take turns with your child pointing to people and things in your home and saying the nouns that name them.

6   **Conventions** Nouns: People, Animals, and Things   **1.6.A.2** Identify words that name persons (nouns). **1.6.A.4** Identify words that name things (nouns). **1.20.A.2.iii** Understand and use nouns (common) in the context of reading, writing, and speaking.

Name _____

Trace and **write** the letters. Make sure you write your letters the correct size.

School + Home **Home Activity** Your child practiced writing *S* and *s*. Have your child cut out pictures from old magazines Sam objects that begin with *s* and paste them onto a sheet of paper and label each with the letter *s*.

1.21.A.1 Form upper-case letters legibly in text, using the basic conventions of print (left-to-right and top-to-bottom progression), including spacing between words and sentences. **Also 1.1.B.1, 1.1.B.2, 1.21.A.2.**

Sam

Name _____

Circle the group that could be a real word.

1. 3576   (bike)   t31m   1234   o471

2. (road)   2021   88bt   976a   54em

3. 2631   3142   987c   mm32   (pony)

4. 4226   K310   (look)   n325   7624

Look at the first group of letters. **Circle** the group of letters that is in the same order as the first group.

5. (nap)   (nap)   pna   ban

6. (tap)   pat   (tap)   apt

7. (mad)   dam   (mad)   mda

8. (pin)   nip   (pin)   inp

 School + Home **Home Activity** Your child identified groups of letters and compared the sequence of letters in words or letter groups such as *pat, tap,* and *apt.* Write the letters of your child's name in different orders. Have your child identify the name with the letters in correct sequence.

8 Print Awareness

1.1.A 1. Recognize that spoken words are represented in written English by specific sequences of letters.

Name _____

Tt

Say the word for each picture.
Write t on the line if the word has the same first sound as .

1. T t

2. D b

3. S s

4. R r

5. T t

6. M m

7. S s

8. T t

School + Home **Home Activity** Your child learned that some words begin with the letter *t*. Have your child find other words with /t/ as in *tiger*.

1.2.E.1 Isolate initial sounds in one-syllable spoken words. **Also 1.2.E.3.**

Phonics Consonant *Tt/t/*   9

Name _____

Read the words in the box.
Pick a word to finish each sentence.
Write it on the line.
Read the sentence from left to right.

I   see   a   green

1. This is ___A___ .

2. We _____ a .

3. This is my _____ .

4. _____ am a .

Home Activity This week your child learned to identify and read the words *I, see, a,* and *green*. As you read with your child, encourage him or her to point out these words in print.

10   High-Frequency Words

⊕ **1.3.H.1** Identify at least 100 high-frequency words from a commonly used list. **Also 1.3.H.2.**

Nouns: People, Animals, and Things

Tell about your room.
Finish the sentences.
Use words from the box or your own words.

| a bed   a rug   a lamp   books   a cat |

_____

I have _____ in my room.

_____

I have _____ in my room.

_____

I have _____ in my room.

Find other nouns. **Say** a sentence for each noun.

Home Activity Your child learned how to use nouns for people and things in writing. Have your child write a sentence about people and things in another room in your home. Ask your child to identify the nouns in the sentence.

1.6.A.2 Identify words that name persons (nouns). **1.6.A.4**
Identify words that name things (nouns). **1.20.A.2.iii** Understand and
use nouns (common) in the context of reading, writing, and speaking.

Conventions Nouns: People, Animals, and Things **11**

Name _____

Trace and **write** the letters. Make sure you write your letters the correct size.

Home Activity Your child practiced writing *T* and *t*. Say names and words that begin with *T* and *t* and have your child write the correct letter each time you say a name or word.

1.21.A.1 Form upper-case letters legibly in text, using the basic conventions of print (left-to-right and top-to-bottom progression), including spacing between words and sentences. **Also 1.1.B.1, 1.1.B.2, 1.21.A.2.**

Name _____

Circle the group that could be a real word.

1.   5628   history   s42p   12345   u572

2.   3023   science   66cv   786i   63fn

3.   6432   3543   786d   number   kk41

4.   2435   S221   woman   m245   6734

Look at the first group of letters. **Circle** the group of letters that is in the same order as the first group.

5.   pit   pit   tip   pti

6.   sag   ags   gas   sag

7.   nip   imp   nip   pin

8.   tip   pit   tpi   tip

Home Activity Your child identified groups of letters and compared the sequence of letters in words or letter groups such as such as *pit, tip,* and *pti.* Make individual letter cards with the letters of your child's name. Ask your child to put the letters in correct sequence.

1.1.A 1. Recognize that spoken words are represented in written English by specific sequences of letters.

Name _____

Aa

Say the word for each picture.
Write a on the line if the word has the same first sound as that apple.

1.	(alligator)	2.	(ant)
3.	(sun)	4.	(tent)
5.	(astronaut)	6.	(mitten)

Say the word for each picture.
Write a on the line to complete the word.

7. s t

8. m t

✦ 1.2 Display phonological awareness. **Also** 1.2.D.1, 1.2.E.1, 1.2.E.3, 1.2.F.1.

Name _____

Read the story.
Draw the most important character from the story.

Blue Jay found some beautiful peacock feathers.

Blue Jay tied the feathers to his tail.

He thought he looked grand.

He strutted in front of the other jays.

The jays pulled out his peacock feathers.

Then they all flew away from Blue Jay.

Blue Jay knew then: No one likes a showoff.

Home Activity Your child read a fable (fiction) and identified the main character. Read a fiction story with your child. Have your child name the most important character (or characters) in the story. Ask your child to tell you what the character looks like and how the character acts.

1.9 Understand the structure and elements of fiction.

Name _____

Nouns: People, Animals, and Things

Mark the sentence that has a line under a noun that names
a person, an animal, or a thing.

1. ○ They <u>sat</u> on the bed.
   ○ They sat <u>on</u> the bed.
   ○ They sat on the <u>bed</u>.

2. ○ She is with her <u>mom</u>.
   ○ She <u>is</u> with her mom.
   ○ She is <u>with</u> her mom.

3. ○ He can read <u>a</u> book.
   ○ He can read a <u>book</u>.
   ○ He can <u>read</u> a book.

4. ○ The boy <u>plays</u> with a pet.
   ○ The boy plays <u>with</u> a pet.
   ○ The boy plays with a <u>pet</u>.

School + Home

Home Activity Your child prepared for taking tests on nouns for people or things. Read a story together. Have your child point out nouns that name people or things in the story.

✪ **1.6.A.2** Identify words that name persons (nouns). **1.6.A.4** Identify words that name things (nouns). **1.20.A.2.iii** Understand and use nouns (common) in the context of reading, writing, and speaking.

Name _____

Circle the front cover.

Sam

Sam

Place an X over the back cover.

The cat
got up.

Circle the book that Sam wrote.

The
Sad Cat
by
Sam

My Cat
by
Dan

School + Home

Home Activity Your child learned to identify the front cover, back cover, and title page of a book. Have your child point out the front and back covers and title page of the next book you read together.

1.24.B.1 Use the text features in age-appropriate reference works to locate information.

Research Parts of a Book   **17**

Trace and **write** the letters. Make sure you write your letters the correct size.

A a

Copy the words. **Write** the letters from left to right.

Sam

mat

am

as

Tam

sat

at

Matt

School + Home

Home Activity Your child practiced writing words with *Aa*. Have your child draw a picture of two of the words he or she wrote and label the pictures with the words.

1.21.A.1 Form upper-case letters legibly in text, using the basic conventions of print (left-to-right and top-to-bottom progression), including spacing between words and sentences. **Also 1.1.B.1, 1.1.B.2, 1.21.A.2.**

© Pearson Education, Inc. 1

Circle the group that could be a real word.

1. 9546   r2nf   23456   match   t4ms

2. 6237   pancake   e9bg   5769   oh77

3. girls   2531   9213   43cd   jj33

4. 8762   2310   table   n22p   5148

Look at the first group of letters. **Circle** the group of letters that is in the same order as the first group.

5. pot   pot   top   opt

6. ten   net   ten   ent

7. bat   tab   abt   bat

8. sat   tar   sta   sat

Home Activity Your child looked at the letter sequence in words and compared the sequence of letters in words or letter groups such as *pot, top,* and *opt.* Look at item 1 with your child. Have your child explain his answer.

1.1.A 1. Recognize that spoken words are represented in written English by specific sequences of letters.

Print Awareness   19

Name _____

Read the words in the box.
Pick a word to finish each sentence.
Write it on the line.
Read the sentence from left to right.

I   see   a   green

1. _____ have a _____ .

2. The _____ is _____ .

3. I _____ the _____ .

4. This is _____ _____ .

Home Activity This week your child identified and read the words *I, see, a,* and *green.* Write each word on a card. Have your child read each word and then use it in a sentence.

20   High-Frequency Words

1.3.H.1 Identify at least 100 high-frequency words from a commonly used list. **Also 1.3.H.2.**

Cc

Say the word for each picture.
Write c on the line if the word has the same first sound as .

1.
_____

2.
_____

3.
_____

4.
_____

5.
_____

6.
_____

7.
_____

8.
_____

School + Home

Home Activity Your child learned that some words begin with the letter *c*. Have your child find other words with /k/ as in *cat*.

1.2.E.1 Isolate initial sounds in one-syllable spoken words. **Also 1.2.E.3, 1.3.A.2.i.2.**

Phonics Consonant Cc/k/   **21**

Name _____

Look at each set of pictures.
Circle the picture that shows a place.

1.

2.

3.

4.

5.

School + Home

Home Activity Your child learned about places in a story. As you read together, have your child tell you what he or she knows about the setting of the story.

22 Comprehension Setting

1.9 Understand the structure and elements of fiction.

Name _____

Trace and **write** the letters. Make sure you write your letters the correct size.

C   c

C

Č

Copy the words. **Write** the letters from left to right.

Mac _____   sat _____

Cam _____   Tam _____

cat _____   tat _____

mat _____   Sam _____

Home Activity Your child practiced writing words with *Cc*. Have your child choose two words from the box and write them on a separate piece of paper.

1.21.A.1 Form upper-case letters legibly in text, using the basic conventions of print (left-to-right and top-to-bottom progression), including spacing between words and sentences. **Also 1.1.B.1, 1.1.B.2, 1.21.A.2.**

Handwriting 23

Name _____

Snap!

Look at the first group of letters. **Circle** the group of letters that is in the same order as the first group.

1.
   top

   top   pot   opt

2.
   net

   ten   net   ent

3.
   tag

   got   agt   tag

4.
   yam

   yam   may   yma

5.
   pan

   nap   pan   npa

6.
   bag

   bga   gab   bag

School + Home **Home Activity** Your child looked at the letter sequence in words and compared the sequence of letters in words or letter groups such as *top, pot,* and *opt.* Have your child identify the sequence of letters of each pictured word. Then say the word with your child.

1.1.A 1. Recognize that spoken words are represented in written English by specific sequences of letters.

Name _____

Pp

Say the word for each picture.
Write p on the line if the word has the same first sound as

1. _ _ _ _ _ _

2. _ _ _ _ _ _

3. _ _ _ _ _ _

4. _ _ _ _ _ _

Say the word for each picture.
Write p on the line if the word has the same ending sound as .

5. _ _ **ma**

6. _ _ **Sa**

7. _ _ **ca**

8. _ _ **sa**

 School + Home

Home Activity Your child learned that some words begin and end with the letter p. Have your child find other words that begin and end with /p/.

1.2.E.2 Isolate medial sounds in one-syllable spoken words.
Also 1.2.E.1, 1.2.E.3, 1.3.A.2.i.14.

Nouns: Places

A **noun** also names a place.

The word **school** names a place.

The word **store** names a place.

Draw a line from the noun to the correct picture.
Say a sentence for each noun.

1. zoo

2. park

3. lake

4. library

 School + Home

Home Activity Your child learned about nouns that name places. Have your child identify places in his or her neighborhood.

1.6.A.3 Identify words that name places (nouns). **1.20.A.2.iii** Understand and use nouns (common) in the context of reading, writing, and speaking.

Name _____

Trace and **write** the letters. Make sure you write your letters the correct size.

P   p

P

p

Copy the words. **Write** the tall and small letters the correct size. **Write p** so that it falls below the line.

Pam _____   map _____

Pat _____   sap _____

tap _____   cap _____

School + Home

Home Activity Your child practiced writing words with *Pp*. Say these words to your child: *Pennsylvania, Peter, Patrick, pickle, plum, pet.* Have your child write *P* or *p* to show how each word begins.

1.21.A.1 Form upper-case letters legibly in text, using the basic conventions of print (left-to-right and top-to-bottom progression), including spacing between words and sentences. **Also 1.21.A.2.**

Name _____

Trace the arrows.
Connect the word trains from left to right and top to bottom.

START:

I like green.

We see one.

See the one.

We like green.

END

Home Activity Your child learned that reading is done from top to bottom, and from left to right with a return sweep. Show your child a page from a favorite book. Have him or her point to each word from left to right, then return to the beginning of the next line and move again from left to right.

28 **Print Awareness**

🟠 **1.1. E.1** Read texts by moving from top to bottom of page.
Also 1.1.E.2.

Nn

Say the word for each picture.
Write n on the line if the word has the same first sound as .

1.

2.

3.

4.

Say the word for each picture.
Write n on the line if the word has the same ending sound as .

5. ma

6. ca

7. ma

8. ca

Home Activity Your child learned that some words begin and end with the letter *n*. Have your child find other words that begin and end with /n/.

1.2 Display phonological awareness. **Also 1.3.A.2.i.13.**

Name _____

Read the words in the box.
Pick a word to finish each sentence.
Write it on the line.

| we | like | the | one |

1. _____ see a .

2. Tip is on _____ .

3. I have _____ .

4. I _____ our .

Home Activity This week your child identified and read the words *we, like, the,* and *one.* As you read with your child, encourage him or her to point out these words in print.

1.3.H.1 Identify at least 100 high-frequency words from a commonly used list. **Also 1.3.H.2.**

Name _____

Nouns: Places

Tell about places you go with your family.
Finish the sentences.
Use words from the box or your own words.

| store | playground | park | zoo |

My family and I go to the _____.

_____.

My family and I go to the _____.

_____.

My family and I go to the _____.

Find other nouns. **Say** a sentence for each noun.

Home Activity Your child learned how to use nouns for places in writing. Have your child write two sentences that tell about a place he or she would like to go. Ask your child to identify the noun he or she used.

1.6.A.3 Identify words that name places (nouns) **1.20.A.2.iii**
Understand and use nouns (common) in the context of reading, writing, and speaking.

Conventions Nouns: Places **31**

Name _____

Trace and **write** the letters. Make sure you write your letters the correct size.

Copy the words. **Write** the letters from left to right.

Nan

nap

man

tan

Nat

can

pan

mat

Home Activity Your child practiced writing words with *Nn*. Have your child find all the words above that have an *N* or *n* in them and practice writing them one more time.

🌐 **1.21.A.1** Form upper-case letters legibly in text, using the basic conventions of print (left-to-right and top-to-bottom progression), including spacing between words and sentences. **Also 1.21.A.2.**

Name _____

Trace the arrows.
Connect the word trains from left to right and top to bottom.

START:

END

Home Activity Your child learned that reading is done from top to bottom, and from left to right with a return sweep. Show your child a page from a favorite book. Have him or her tell you where to start reading a sentence (left) and in which direction to read (to the right). Remind your child that reading starts at the top and goes to the bottom of the page.

Name _____

Say the word for each picture.
Write the letter on the line that begins the word.

Write p or **n** on the line to complete the word.

Home Activity Your child reviewed words that begin with *c*, *n*, and *p* and reviewed words that end with *n* and *p*. Have your child find other words with /c/ as in *cat*, /p/ as in *pig*, and /n/ as in *nut*.

34 **Phonics** Consonants *Cc/c/, Pp/p/, Nn/n/*

1.2.E.1 Isolate initial sounds in one-syllable spoken words.
Also 1.2.E.3, 1.2.F.1.

Name _____

Read the story.
Draw a picture that shows where the story takes place.

Mei and Jake walk in the warm sand.

Waves splash their bare feet.

Mei and Jake decide to make a sand castle.

They make thick walls and tall towers.

The children stand up to look at their castle.

Suddenly a giant wave comes to shore!

Now the castle is gone.

Home Activity Your child read a story (fiction) and then identified where the story takes place (setting). Have your child name one or two favorite stories. Help your child identify the setting of each story.

1.9 Understand the structure and elements of fiction.

Nouns: Places

Mark the noun for a place that completes the sentence.

1. We see animals at the _____.
   - ○ zoo
   - ○ fish
   - ○ eat

2. Sam and Tam swim in the _____.
   - ○ cat
   - ○ dip
   - ○ lake

3. Tip can run in the _____.
   - ○ park
   - ○ man
   - ○ pet

4. The _____ has a big yard.
   - ○ call
   - ○ baby
   - ○ home

Home Activity Your child prepared for taking tests on nouns for places. Read a story together. Have your child point out the nouns that name places.

1.6.A.3 Identify words that name places (nouns). **1.20.A.2.iii** Understand and use nouns (common) in the context of reading, writing, and speaking.

Animal Families
Contents

Use this **table of contents** from a social studies book to find information.

1. **Draw** a circle around the page numbers.

2. **Draw** a box around the chapter titles.

3. **Write** the name of Chapter 5.

_____

- -

_____

4. **Write** the page number on which the chapter "Zebras and Foals" begins.

_____

- - - - - - - - - - - - - - - - -

_____

5. **Write** how many chapters are listed.

_____

- - - - - - - - - - - - - - - - -

_____

Home Activity Your child learned to use the table of contents in a book to find information. As you read together, point out the table of contents and encourage your child to help you find information such as the page number for a specific chapter.

1.24.B.1 Use the text features in age-appropriate references works to locate information.

Research Parts of a Book   37

Name _____

Copy the words. Make sure you write your tall and small letters the correct size. Remember **p** falls below the line.

Nan _____

man _____

pan _____

Sam _____

tan _____

cat _____

Pam _____

tap _____

sat _____

pat _____

can _____

mat _____

Mac _____

map _____

sap _____

Cam _____

Ann _____

cap _____

Home Activity Your child practiced writing words with *Aa, Mm, Ss, Tt, Cc, Pp*, and *Nn*. Have your child choose a word that begins with the letter *p* from the list and then write the word. Repeat for the letters *m, s, t, c,* and *n*.

1.21.A.1 Form upper-case letters legibly in text, using the basic conventions of print (left-to-right and top-to-bottom progression), including spacing between words and sentences. **Also 1.21.A.2.**

Name _____

Underline the name of the book.

Place an X over the book about Sam.

Circle the book that Nan wrote.
Draw a box around the book that Pam drew pictures for.

 Home Activity Your child learned to use the information on a book cover and title page to figure out what the book is about. Point out the cover and title page of the next book you read together. Explain that the title tells what the book is about.

1.1.F.1 Identify information different parts of a book provide.

Name _____

Read the words in the box.
Pick a word to finish each sentence.
Write it on the line.

| we | like | the | one |

1. Here is _____ man.

2. I _____ to run with my .

3. I have _____ too.

4. _____ have a and a .

Home Activity This week your child identified and read the words *we, like, the,* and *one.* Write each word on a card. Have your child read each word and then use it in a sentence.

40 **High-Frequency Words**

1.3.H.2 Read at least 100 high-frequency words from a commonly used list. **Also 1.3.H.1.**

Ff

Say the word for each picture.
Write f on the line if the word has the same first sound as .

1. _____
   _____

2. _____
   _____

3. _____
   _____

4. _____
   _____

5. _____
   _____

6. _____
   _____

7. _____
   _____

8. _____
   _____

School + Home

Home Activity Your child learned that some words begin with the letter *f*. Have your child find other words with /f/ as in *fish*.

⊕ **1.2.E.1** Isolate initial sounds in one-syllable spoken words.
Also 1.2.E.2, 1.2.E.3, 1.3.A.2.i.5.

Phonics Consonant *Ff*/f/   **41**

Name _____

Look at the pictures.
Tell a story about the pictures.
Draw a picture to tell what happens next.

Home Activity Your child learned that the plot tells what happens in a story. Have your child tell you a story about the pictures on this page. Help your child by asking what happens in the beginning Tif the story, in the middle, and at the end.

42 **Comprehension** Plot

🔄 **1.9.A.1** Describe the plot (problem and solution).

Name _____

Trace and **write** the letters. Make sure you write your letters the correct size.

F

f

Copy the words. **Write** the letters the correct size.

Fam

fan

pat

sat

Ann

fat

nap

man

Home Activity Your child practiced writing words with *Ff*. Have your child choose two words from above that begin with *f* and practice writing the words again.

1.21.A.1 Form upper-case letters legibly in text, using the basic conventions of print (left-to-right and top-to-bottom progression), including spacing between words and sentences. **Also 1.21.A.2.**

Name _____

Underline the name of the person who wrote the book.
Circle the name of the person who drew the pictures.

Sit Sam Sit

By Dan Buck

Drawings by
Tim Mix

Circle the book that Kim Fin wrote.

Sit Sam Sit

By Dan Buck

Drawings by
Tim Mix

Jam for Pam

By Kim Fin

Drawings by
Pat Kip

Place an X over the book about Tam.

Sam

by Tip

Tam

by Mat

School + Home

Home Activity Your child learned to use the information on a book cover and title page to figure out what the book is about. Your child also learned to look for the name of the author and illustrator of a book. Discuss illustrations in a favorite book with your child.

1.1.F.1 Identify information different parts of a book provide.

Bb

Say the word for each picture.
Write b on the line if the word has the same first sound as .

1. _____

2. _____

3. _____

4. _____

5. _____

6. _____

Write two words that rhyme with **nab**.

7. t _____

8. c _____

School + Home

Home Activity Your child learned that some words begin and end with the letter b. Have your child find other words with /b/ as in *balloon*.

1.2.E.1 Isolate initial sounds in one-syllable spoken words.
Also 1.2.E.2, 1.2.E.3, 1.3.A.2.i.1.

Name _____

Verbs

A **verb** names an action. It tells what a person or thing does.

The dog **eats**. **Eats** is the verb.

Circle the verb in each sentence.

1. Sam and Tip run in the yard.

2. The cat hit the bag.

3. They play with the bag.

4. The cat fit in a bag.

5. Tam hid in the bag.

Find other verbs. **Say** a sentence for each verb.

✦ **1.6.A.1** Identify words that name actions (verbs). **1.20.A.1.ii** Understand and use verbs (present) in the context of reading, writing, and speaking.

Name _____

Trace and **write** the letters. Make sure you write your letters the correct size.

B B

b b

Copy the words. Sit and hold your paper the correct way.

Bab

bat

Tab

bam

nab

ban

cab

fat

Home Activity Your child practiced writing words with *Bb*. Have your child choose a word from above with *B* and a word with *b* and practice writing each three times as neatly as possible.

1.21.A.1 Form upper-case letters legibly in text, using the basic conventions of print (left-to-right and top-to-bottom progression), including spacing between words and sentences. **Also 1.21.A.2.**

Handwriting 47

Name _____

Underline the title of the book.

Circle who wrote the book.

Circle the book that Peg Bud wrote.
Draw a box around the book that Ken Fox drew the pictures for.

Home Activity Your child learned to use the information on a book cover and title page to figure out what the book is about. Your child also learned to look for the name of the author and illustrator of a book. On a book your child enjoys, point out the cover and title page. Point to the name of the author and read it aloud.

48 **Print Awareness**

🔶 1.1.F.1 Identify the information that different parts of a book provide.

Name _____

Gg

Say the word for each picture.
Write g on the line if the word has the same first sound as .

1. _____

2. _____

3. _____

4. _____

Write four words that rhyme with **gag.**

5. **s** _____

6. **n** _____

7. **t** _____

8. **b** _____

1.2 Display phonological awareness. **Also 1.3.A.2.i.6.**

Name _____

Read the words in the box.
Pick a word to finish each sentence.
Write it on the line.

| do | look | you | was | yellow |

1. Tip _____ sad. _____

2. _____ in the _____.

3. _____ you see the _____?

4. The _____ is _____.

5. _____ can hold the _____.

Home Activity This week your child identified and read the words *do, look, you, was,* and *yellow.* As you read with your child, encourage him or her to point out these words in print.

1.3.H.1 Identify at least 100 high-frequency words from a commonly used list. **Also 1.3.H.2.**

Name _____

Verbs

Tell about things you do in the yard.
Finish the sentences.
Use words from the box or your own words.

> ride a bike   run   play catch   jump rope

_____

I _____ in the yard.

_____

I _____ in the yard.

_____

I _____ in the yard.

Say a sentence to tell what you like to do.

1.6.A.1 Identify words that name actions (verbs). **1.20.A.1.ii**
Understand and use verbs (present) in the context of reading, writing, and speaking.

Name _____

Trace and **write** the letters. Make sure you write your letters the correct size.

G g

G

g

Copy the words.

Gam _____   nag _____

bag _____   gas _____

tag _____   gab _____

Did you write the letter **g** so that it falls below the line each time?

| Yes | | No |

Home Activity Your child practiced writing words with *Gg*. Say the following words: *Gus, Gary, Gwen, girl, give, get.* Have your child write *G* or *g* to show how each word begins.

1.21.A.1 Form upper-case letters legibly in text, using the basic conventions of print (left-to-right and top-to-bottom progression), including spacing between words and sentences. **Also 1.21.A.2.**

Name _____

a b c d e f g h i j k l m n o p q r s t u v w x y z

Circle the letter that comes first in the alphabet.

1.	2.	3.
s t a	c p n	f b g

4.	5.	6.
n a g	s f p	t g n

Write the letters in alphabetical order.

7. m a s	8. t c p	9. n f b g

10. t g n	11. s c f	12. n a p f

Home Activity Your child learned to put letters in alphabetical order. Write three different letters on index cards, one letter on each card. Have your child put the letters in alphabetical order.

Name _____

Ii

Say the word for each picture.

Write **i** on the line if the word has the same first sound as .

1.

2.

3.

4.

Say the word for each picture.

Write **i** on the line if the word has the same middle sound as .

5. c___t

6. b___g

7. p___n

8. b___n

Home Activity Your child learned that some words have the short *i* sound. Have your child find other words with /i/ at the beginning or in the middle, such as *ink* and *sit*.

1.2 Display phonological awareness. **Also 1.2.E.1, 1.2.E.2, 1.2.E.3.**

Name _____

Read the story.
Circle the picture that shows what happened next.

Maria put on her baseball uniform.

Dad helped Maria find her baseball cap.

Then Maria and Dad got in the car.

Dad drove to the baseball field.

Maria ran over to her team, the Hawks.

The coach told Maria to pick up a bat.

 Home Activity Your child read a story and then identified the events that happen, or the plot, in the story. Read a fiction story with your child and have your child tell you the important events in the story.

1.9 Understand the structure and elements of fiction.

Genre/Literary Analysis 55

Name _____

Verbs

Mark the sentence that has a line under the verb.

1. ○ Sam jumps in the ba<u>g</u>.
   ○ Sam <u>jumps</u> in the bag.
   ○ <u>Sam</u> jumps in the bag.

2. ○ She can <u>tap</u> the bag.
   ○ She can tap the ba<u>g</u>.
   ○ She can tap the bag.
   ﹍

3. ○ <u>She</u> can see the hat.
   ○ She can <u>see</u> the hat.
   ○ She can see the <u>hat</u>.

4. ○ He can play <u>here</u>.
   ○ He <u>can</u> play here.
   ○ He can <u>play</u> here.

Home Activity Your child prepared for taking tests on verbs. Read a story together. Have your child point out the verbs in the story.

1.6.A.1 Identify words that name actions (verbs). **1.20.A.1.ii** Understand and use verbs (present) in the context of reading, writing, and speaking.

Name _____

Read each question. **Circle** the correct answer.

1. This sign tells you how fast to go.

2. This sign tells you not to go.

3. What does this sign mean?

     eat here   do not speed   stop

4. What does this sign mean?

     police   library   hospital

5. Which sign would help you if you were sick?

 Home Activity Your child learned the meanings of many different signs. Take a walk in the neighborhood and point out the different signs you see on the road or street. See how many of the signs your child can explain.

1.15.B Explain the meaning of specific signs and symbols.

Research Signs **57**

Name _____

Trace and **write** the letters. Make sure you write your letters the correct size.

Copy the words. Write the tall and small letters the correct size. Write **p** and **g** so that they fall below the line.

If

sit

pan

tap

pig

big

Home Activity Your child practiced writing words with *Ii*. Have your child think of words that rhyme with *pig*. Then help your child write two of the rhyming words: *big, dig, fig, rig, wig.*

58 **Handwriting**

Name _____

a b c d e f g h i j k l m n o p q r s t u v w x y z

Circle the letter that comes first in the alphabet.

1.	2.	3.
s t i	a p n	f c g

4.	5.	6.
g s f	n i p	t g n

Write the letters in alphabetical order.

7. b a g	8. p c i	9. g f b
_____	_____	_____
- - - - - - - -	- - - - - - - -	- - - - - - - -

10. p a s	11. n c i	12. t f b
_____	_____	_____
- - - - - - - -	- - - - - - - -	- - - - - - - -

Home Activity Your child learned to put letters in alphabetical order. Write three different letters on index cards, one letter on each card. Have your child put the letters in alphabetical order, and then write them in order.

1.1.C.1 Sequence the letters of the alphabet.

Name _____

Read the words in the box.
Pick a word to finish each sentence.
Write it on the line.

| do | look | you | was | yellow |

1. This is _____ ⎯⎯⎯⎯⎯⎯⎯⎯⎯⎯⎯ .

2. Can _____ see the ?

3. _____ at that big _____ !

4. The _____ in the bag!

5. _____ you like my ?

Home Activity This week your child learned to read the words *do, look, you, was,* and *yellow.* Write each word on a card. Have your child read each word and then use it in a sentence.

1.3.H.1 Identify at least 100 high-frequency words from a commonly used list. **Also 1.3.H.2.**

Name _____

Dd

Say the word for each picture.
Write **d** on the line if the word has the same first sound as .

1. _____

2. _____

3. _____

4. _____

Say the word for each picture.
Write **d** on the line if the word has the same ending sound as .

5. _____

6. _____

7. _____

8. _____

 School + Home
Home Activity Your child learned that some words begin and end with the letter *d*. Have your child find other words that begin and end with /d/.

Name _____

Circle the make-believe pictures.
Draw a box around the real pictures.

1.

2.

3.

4.

5.

6.

Home Activity Your child looked at pictures to tell which may be real and which may be make-believe. Have your child draw a picture of something that is make-believe and then draw a picture of something that is real.

1.9 Make inferences about the structure and elements of fiction.

Name _____

Trace and **write** the letters. Make sure you write your letters the correct size.

D d

D

d

Copy the words. **Write** the letters the correct size.

Dan _____

fad _____

Dad _____

bad _____

dip _____

pad _____

dig _____

Sid _____

Home Activity Your child practiced writing words with *Dd*. Have your child choose a word from above with *D* and a word with *d* and then write the words as neatly as possible.

1.21.A.1 Form upper-case letters legibly in text, using the basic conventions of print (left-to-right and top-to-bottom progression), including spacing between words and sentences. **Also 1.21.A.2.**

Name _____

Circle the title of the book.
Underline the author of the book.
Draw a box around the illustrator of the book.

Three Pups

By Sue Green

Illustrated by
Mick Bell

Circle the book that Bess Dell wrote.
Draw a box around the book that Tom Lock illustrated.

Nuts

By Bess Dell

Illustrated by
Ron Ness

Fog

By Rex Dab

Illustrated by
Tom Lock

Home Activity Your child learned to use the information on a book cover and title page to figure out what the book is about. Your child also learned to look for the name of the author and illustrator of a book. On a book your child enjoys, point out the cover and title page. Point to the name of the illustrator and read it aloud. Discuss the illustrations and invite your child to express an opinion about the illustrator.

1.1.F.1 Identify the information that different parts of a book provide.

Name _____

L l

Say the word for each picture.

Write l on the line if the word has the same first sound as .

1.		_____
2.		_____
3.		_____
4.		_____
5.		_____
6.		_____

Write two words that rhyme with **pill**.

7. _____

8. _____

Home Activity Your child learned that some words begin with the letter *l*. Have your child find other words with /l/ as in *ladder*.

1.2.E.2 Isolate medial sounds in one-syllable spoken words.
Also 1.2.E.1, 1.2.E.3, 1.3.A.2.i.11.

Phonics Consonant *Ll*/*l*/   65

Name _____

Simple Sentences

A **sentence** has a noun and a verb. It tells who did what.

The **dog jumps**.

>   **Dog** is a noun.
>
>   **Jumps** is a verb.

Find the sentence. **Circle** the sentence.

1. The cat can run by Tam.

   run by Tam

2. got the top

   She got the top.

3. The doll is on the mat.

   the doll

4. The cat sat on the mat.

   the mat

Home Activity Your child learned about simple sentences. Have your child find things in your house to make sentences about. Have your child identify the parts of his or her sentences.

✪ **1.21.B.1.i** Recognize basic capitalization for the beginning of sentences. **1.21.C.1** Recognize punctuation marks at the end of declarative sentences.

Name _____

Trace and **write** the letters. Make sure you write your letters the correct size.

Copy the words. Sit and hold your paper the correct way.

Lin _____

Cal _____

lid _____

lad _____

pill _____

lip _____

lab _____

mill _____

Home Activity Your child practiced writing *Ll*. Say names and words that begin with *L* or *l* and have your child write the correct letter each time you say a name or word.

1.21.A.1 Form upper-case letters legibly in text, using the basic conventions of print (left-to-right and top-to-bottom progression), including spacing between words and sentences. **Also 1.21.A.2.**

Name _____

a b c d e f g h i j k l m n o p q r s t u v w x y z

Circle the letter that comes first in the alphabet.

1.	2.	3.
a l t	i p n	f d g

4.	5.	6.
t h l	s n p	d c g

Write the letters in alphabetical order.

7. m b s	8. t d p	9. t f b
_____	_____	_____

10. p w n	11. f c i	12. i f b g
_____	_____	_____

Home Activity Your child learned to sequence the letters of the alphabet. Write three different letters in random order. Have your child write the letters in alphabetical order.

⭐ **1.1.C.1** Sequence the letters of the alphabet.

Name _____

Hh

Say the word for each picture.
Write h on the line if the word has the same first sound as

1. _____

2. _____

3. _____

4. _____

5. _____

6. _____

7. _____

8. _____

 School + Home

Home Activity Your child learned that some words begin with the letter *h*. Have your child find other words with /h/ as in *helicopter*.

1.22.A.1. Use phonological knowledge to match sounds to letters to construct words. **Also 1.3.A.2.i.8.**

Name _____

Read the words in the box.

Pick a word to finish each sentence.

Write it on the line. **Remember** to begin a sentence with a capital letter.

are	have	they	that	two

1. _____

    _____ are playing in the [pond] .

2. Look at _____ white [rabbit] .

3. We _____ a little [dog] .

4. My _____ went home.

5. There _____ three [drum] .

Home Activity This week your child identified and read the words *are, have, they, that,* and *two.* As you read with your child, encourage him or her to point out these words in print.

1.3.H.1 Identify at least 100 high-frequency words from a commonly used list. **Also 1.3.H.2.**

Name _____

Simple Sentences

Tell a story about what you like to play with.
Finish the sentence. **Use** words from the box.
Write a sentence of your own.

> a doll   a ball   a toy car   games   a top

I like to play with _____ .

I like to play with _____ .

_____

_____

Say other sentences using the toys.

Home Activity Your child learned how to use simple sentences in writing. Have your child write two sentences that tell how he or she can help clean up a mess.

1.20.A.2.i Recognize and use nouns (singular) in the context of reading, writing, and speaking. **Also 1.1.D.1.**

Name _____

Trace and **write** the letters. Make sure you write your letters the correct size.

H

h

Copy the words.

Halt _____   his _____

Han _____   hat _____

hip _____   hand _____

Did you remember the crossbar on the letter **H**? | **Yes** | | **No** |

Home Activity Your child practiced writing words with *Hh*. Say the following words: *Hal, Hank, Harry, have, him, hit*. Have your child write *H* or *h* to show how each word begins.

1.21.A.1 Form upper-case letters legibly in text, using the basic conventions of print (left-to-right and top-to-bottom progression), including spacing between words and sentences. **Also 1.21.A.2.**

Name _____

a b c d e f g h i j k l m n o p q r s t u v w x y z

Circle the letter that comes first in the alphabet.

1.

i t h

2.

d p n

3.

s b g

4.

t f m

5.

s p t

6.

n g l

Write the letters in alphabetical order.

7. b d g

_____

- - - - - - - - - - - - - -

8. n f l

_____

- - - - - - - - - - - - - -

9. c b p

_____

- - - - - - - - - - - - - -

10. v h s

_____

- - - - - - - - - - - - - -

11. m f o

_____

- - - - - - - - - - - - - -

12. t m b i

_____

- - - - - - - - - - - - - -

Home Activity Your child learned to put words in alphabetical order. Say two different letters in random order. Have your child write the letters in alphabetical order.

🌐 **1.1.C.1** Sequence the letters of the alphabet.

Name _____

Oo

Say the word for each picture.

Write o on the line if the word has the same first sound as ⬤ .

1. _____

2. _____

3. _____

4. _____

Say the word for each picture.

Write o on the line if the word has the same middle sound as ●.

5. t __ p

6. d __ ll

7. p __ n

8. m __ p

School + Home **Home Activity** Your child learned about the short *o* vowel sound in words. Have your child find other words with /o/ at the beginning or in the middle, such as *octopus* and *box*.

🟢 1.2.E.1 Isolate initial sounds in one-syllable words.
Also 1.2.E.2, 1.2.F.1.

Name _____

Read the story. **Circle** the make-believe pictures.
Draw a box around the real pictures.

My friend lives on a farm.

I like to visit the farm.

I help my friend feed the chickens.

We let the cows out of the barn.

One day we pick corn.

There is a lot of work to do on a farm.

1.

2.

3.

4.

5.

6.

Home Activity Your child read a story and then identified pictures of real things and make-believe things. Remind your child that some stories could really happen and some stories are make believe. Have your child draw a picture of a real pig and a make-believe pig.

⬤ 1.9 Understand the structure and elements of fiction.

Genre/Literary Analysis 75

Name _____

Simple Sentences

Mark the group of words that is a sentence.

1. ⊗ look at that green
   ⊗ that green top
   ● Look at that green top.

2. ● The dog will jump.
   ⊗ will jump
   ⊗ the dog

3. ⊗ cat can do
   ● look what the cat
   ⊗ Look what the cat can do.

4. ⊗ Mom can see the
   ● Mom can see the bag.
   ⊗ the bag

School +Home

Home Activity Your child prepared for taking tests on simple sentences. Read a story together. Have your child point out the parts of the sentences.

1.1.D.1 Recognize distinguishing features of a sentence. **1.21.B.1.i** Recognize basic capitalization for the beginning of sentences. **1.21.C.1** Recognize punctuation marks at the end of declarative sentences.

Name _____

Circle the traffic symbols in each row.

1.

2.

Place an X on the symbols that are found on the map.

3.

School + Home

Home Activity Your child has learned to identify traffic and map symbols. Point out traffic symbols when on the road together. Point out map symbols when you look at maps together.

1.15.B.2 Explain the meaning of specific symbols.

Research Traffic and Map Symbols **77**

Name _____

Trace and **write** the letters. Make sure you write your letters the correct size.

O

Ò

Copy the words. **Write** the tall and small letters the correct size. Write **p** and **g** so that they fall below the line.

On

dog

pot

golf

hog

hop

School + Home **Home Activity** Your child practiced writing *Oo*. Say names and words that begin with *O* (*Otto, Oscar, Otis*) and *o* (*only, octopus, ostrich, olive*) and have your child write the correct letter each time you say a name or word.

78 Handwriting

1.21.A.1 Form upper-case letters legibly in text, using the basic conventions of print (left-to-right and top-to-bottom progression), including spacing between words and sentences. **Also 1.21.A.2.**

Name _____

a b c d e f g h i j k l m n o p q r s t u v w x y z

Circle the letter that comes first in the alphabet.

1.	2.	3.
o t d	i p n	s f l

4.	5.	6.
g s f	s o p	t h n

Write the letters in alphabetical order.

7. p o l t	8. t b i a	9. r h v a
‾‾‾‾‾‾	‾‾‾‾‾‾	‾‾‾‾‾‾

10. m u s z	11. g j d c	12. s n a o
‾‾‾‾‾‾	‾‾‾‾‾‾	‾‾‾‾‾‾

Home Activity Your child learned to put words in alphabetical order. Say three different letters in random order. Have your child write the letters in alphabetical order.

✪ 1.1.C.1 Sequence the letters of the alphabet.

Print Awareness 79

Name _____

Read the words in the box.
Pick a word to finish each sentence.
Write it on the line.

| are | have | they | that | two |

1. I like _____ pretty .

2. The _____ all black.

3. Stella has _____ big .

4. Jan and Pete _____ funny .

5. When will _____ go to the ?

1.3.H.1 Identify at least 100 high-frequency words from a commonly used list. **Also 1.3.H.2.**

Name _____

Rr

Say the word for each picture.
Write r on the line if the word has the same first sound as .

1. _____

2. _____

3. _____

4. _____

5. _____

6. _____

7. _____

8. _____

Home Activity Your child learned that some words begin with the letter *r*. Have your child find other words that begin with /r/ as in *rocket*.

1.2.E.1 Isolate initial sounds in one-syllable spoken words. Also 1.3.A.2.i.16.

Name _____

Look at the pictures.

Circle the picture to show what happens next.

Look at the pictures.
Draw a picture of what could happen next.

Home Activity Your child has learned to identify plot, or the events that happen, in a story. When you read a story with your child, have your child retell the important events in the story.

1.9.A.1 Describe the plot (problem and solution).

Name _____

Trace and **write** the letters. Make sure you write your letters the correct size.

R r

R

r

Copy the words. Write the letters the correct size.

Rob _____   rat _____

Ron _____   rod _____

ran _____   rib _____

rip _____   rig _____

School + Home   **Home Activity** Your child practiced writing words with *Rr*. Have your child choose one word with *R* and one word with *r* from above, and practice writing the words one more time.

1.21.A.1 Form upper-case letters legibly in text, using the basic conventions of print (left-to-right and top-to-bottom progression), including spacing between words and sentences. **Also 1.21.A.2.**

Handwriting 83

Name _____

Circle the title of the book.
Underline the author of the book.
Draw a box around the illustrator of the book.

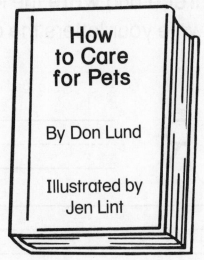

How
to Care
for Pets

By Don Lund

Illustrated by
Jen Lint

Contents

Dogs 3
Cats 10
Fish 18
Birds 24
Rats 36

I. **Draw** a circle around the page numbers.

2. **Put** a box around the chapter titles.

3. **Write** the page number where the chapter about fish begins.

_____

- -

_____

Home Activity Your child learned to use the title, author's name, illustrator's name and the table of contents in a nonfiction book to find information. As you read together, point out the table of contents sand encourage your child to help you find information such as the page number for a specific chapter.

⊕ 1.1.F.1 Identify the information that different parts of a book provide.

Name _____

Jj   Ww

Say the word for each picture.
Write j on the line if the word has the same first sound as .
Write w on the line if the word has the same first sound as [waterfall] .

1.		2.	
3.		4.	
5.		6.	
7.		8.	

School + Home

Home Activity Your child learned that some words begin with the letter *w* and some words begin with the letter *j*. Have your child find other words that begin with /w/ as in *waterfall* and /j/ as in *jet*.

1.2.E.1 Isolate initial sounds in one-syllable spoken words.
Also 1.3.A.2.i.9, 1.3.A.2.i.21.

Phonics Consonants *Ww*/w/ and *Jj*/j/   **85**

Name _____

Adjectives

An **adjective** tells about a person, place, or thing.

a **big** book

Read the sentence.
Circle the adjective.

1. Sam sees the yellow bus.

2. Sam has a big bag.

3. He met fun friends.

4. We read new books.

5. Jill can play with the red ball.

Say each word you circled in a sentence.

Home Activity Your child learned about adjectives. Have your child choose objects from home and use an adjective to describe each one.

🔄 1.20.A.3 Understand and use descriptive adjectives in the context of reading, writing, and speaking.

Name _____

Trace and **write** the letters.
Make sure you write your letters
the correct size.

W _____

W _____

J _____

j _____

Home Activity Your child practiced writing letters *Ww* and *Jj*. Have your child practice writing all four letters three more times. Make sure he or she writes the *j* so that it has a dot above it and falls below the line.

1.21.A.1 Form upper-case letters legibly in text, using the basic conventions of print (left-to-right and top-to-bottom progression), including spacing between words and sentences. **Also 1.21.A.2.**

Name _____

Circle the title of the book.
Underline the author of the book.
Draw a box around the illustrator of the book.

Ant Jobs

By Pat Lund

Illustrated by
Gus Kit

Contents

Ants That Lay Eggs.	3
Ants That Are Dads	10
Ants That Dig	16
Ants That Find Food	24
Ants That Plant Food	36

1. **Draw** a circle around the page numbers.

2. **Put** a box around the chapter titles.

3. **Write** the page number where the chapter about Ants That

Dig begins. _____

Home Activity Your child learned to use the title, author's name, illustrator's name and the table of contents in a nonfiction book to find information. Point out the information on the cover and the table of contents in an interesting book. Encourage your child to count the number of chapters, find the page number for a specific chapter, and turn to that page.

🟢 1.1.F.1 Identify the information that different parts of a book provide.

Name _____

Kk

Say the word for each picture.
Write **k** on the line if the word has the same first sound as .

1. _____

2. _____

3. _____

4. _____

5. _____

6. _____

Pick a word to finish each sentence.
Write the word on the line.

Kim   kiss   kit

7. Sam will _____ Mom.

8. _____ will hit the rim with the .

Home Activity Your child learned that some words begin with the letter *k*. Have your child find other words that begin with /k/ as in *kitten*.

1.2.E.1 Isolate initial sounds in one-syllable spoken words.
Also 1.2.F.1, 1.3.A.2.i.10.

Phonics Consonants *Kk/k/*   89

Name _____

Read the words in the box.

Pick a word to finish each sentence.

Write it on the line. **Remember** to begin each sentence with a capital letter.

| he | is | to | with | three |

1. She _____ on the .

2. Bill came _____ .

3. We have _____ books.

 4. My _____ are _____ me.

5. _____ has a cat.

School + Home   **Home Activity** This week your child identified and read the words *he, is, to, with,* and *three.* As you read with your child, encourage him or her to point out these words in print.

1.3.H.2 Read at least 100 high-frequency words from a commonly used list. **Also 1.3.H.1.**

Name _____

Adjectives

Tell about your room at school.
Finish the sentences. **Use** words from the box.
Write a sentence of your own.

> big   small   nice   new

The room is _____.

The room is _____.

_____.

_____.

Say other sentences using the adjectives in the box.

Home Activity Your child learned how to use adjectives in writing. Have your child write two sentences that describe his or her favorite toy. Ask your child to identify the adjectives in the sentences.

1.20.A.3 Understand and use descriptive adjectives in the context
of reading, writing, and speaking.

Name _____

Trace and **write** the letters. Make sure you write your letters the correct size.

K K

K

k

Copy the words.

Kip _____   kid _____

tack _____   sock _____

kiss _____   Kim _____

Did you write each **K** and **k** the correct size? | **Yes** | | **No** |

School + Home **Home Activity** Your child practiced writing words with *Kk*. Say the following words: *Kim, Karen, Kevin, kite, kitchen, kitten.* Have your child write *K* or *k* to show how each word begins.

🌐 **1.21.A.1** Form upper-case letters legibly in text, using the basic conventions of print (left-to-right and top-to-bottom progression), including spacing between words and sentences. **Also 1.21.A.2.**

Name _____

a b c d e f g h i j k l m n o p q r s t u v w x y z

Circle the letter that comes first in the alphabet.

1.

w   j   e

2.

k   i   r

3.

s   c   l

4.

o   n   h

5.

f   n   m

6.

p   d   g

Write the letters in alphabetical order.

7. y   p   e   s

_____

- - - - - - - - - - - -

_____

8. g   i   f   a

_____

- - - - - - - - - - - -

_____

9. t   x   m   b

_____

- - - - - - - - - - - -

_____

10. q   o   m   r

_____

- - - - - - - - - - - -

_____

11. t   n   l   o

_____

- - - - - - - - - - - -

_____

12. e   a   d   b

_____

- - - - - - - - - - - -

_____

School + Home

Home Activity Your child learned to sequence letters of the alphabet. Say four different letters in random order. Have your child write the letters in alphabetical order. Then give your child five letter cards and have him or her put them in alphabetical order.

1.1.C.1 Sequence the letters of the alphabet.

Name _____

Ee

Say the word for each picture.
Write e on the line if the word has the same first sound as .

1. _____

2. _____

3. _____

4. _____

Say the word for each picture.
Write e on the line if the word has the same middle sound as .

5. _____

6. _____

7. _____

8. _____

 School + Home

Home Activity Your child learned that some words have the short *e* sound. Have your child find other words with /e/ at the beginning or in the middle, such as *elephant* and *bell*.

1.2.E.2 Isolate medial sounds in one-syllable spoken words.
Also 1.2.E.1.

Name _____

Read the story.
Write 1, 2, 3 on the lines to tell what happens in the beginning,
middle, and end.

Lucy plays outside with her puppy.

She wears a big, straw sunhat.

The wind blows the hat off Lucy's head.

So Mom sews ribbons to the hat.

Mom ties the ribbons under Lucy's chin.

Now Lucy's hat stays on.

_____

- - - - - - - - - - - - -

_____

_____

- - - - - - - - - - - - -

_____

_____

- - - - - - - - - - - - -

_____

Home Activity Your child read a story and then identified the order of events that happen in a story. This
story has a problem and solution. Reread the story with your child. Have your child tell you the problem in
the story and how the problem is solved.

Name _____

Adjectives

Mark the sentence that has a line under the adjective.

1. ○ Sam can hop on the <u>big</u> bus.
   ○ <u>Sam</u> can hop on the big bus.
   ○ Sam can <u>hop</u> on the big bus.

2. ○ <u>She</u> is a happy girl.
   ○ She is a happy <u>girl</u>.
   ○ She is a <u>happy</u> girl.

3. ○ We can read a short <u>book</u>.
   ○ We can read a <u>short</u> book.
   ○ We can <u>read</u> a short book.

4. ○ She will eat <u>hot</u> food.
   ○ <u>She</u> will eat hot food.
   ○ She will eat hot <u>food</u>.

Choose other adjectives. **Say** a sentence for each adjective.

School + Home   **Home Activity** Your child prepared for taking tests on adjectives. Read a story together. Have your child identify the adjectives in the story.

1.20.A.3 Understand and use descriptive adjectives in the context of reading, writing, and speaking.

Name _____

Look at the calendar. **Read** the questions.
Circle the answers.

1. What day comes after Monday?

    Sunday   Tuesday   Thursday

2. What day comes after Thursday?

    Wednesday   Saturday   Friday

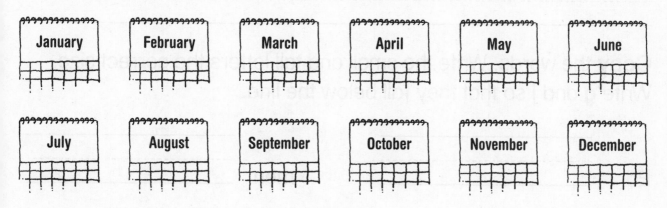

3. What month comes after March?

    April   May   December

4. What month comes after June?

    August   July   October

Home Activity Your child has learned how a calendar shows the order of the days and months. Look at calendars with your child. Have him or her point out the order of the days, weeks, and months.

1.24.B Use text features to locate information.

Name _____

Trace and **write** the letters. Make sure you write your letters the correct size.

E

e

Copy the words. Write the small and tall letters the correct size. Write **g** and **j** so that they fall below the line.

Ed _____

get _____

jet _____

men _____

egg _____

beg _____

Home Activity Your child practiced writing words with *Ee*. Have your child copy the sentence and draw a picture to fill in the blank: *Ed has a pet_____.*

1.21.A.1 Form upper-case letters legibly in text, using the basic conventions of print (left-to-right and top-to-bottom progression), including spacing between words and sentences. **Also 1.21.A.2.**

Name _____

Read each group of words.
Circle the group of words that is a sentence.

---

1. sat fat the a is

Sam can see a cat.

Sam a mad is I

2. The cat is fat.

cat Tam is the

Snap tap cat the

---

3. He cat the on bat

He is on the mat.

mat cat is in nap

4. Tip is with Tam.

cat see Tip can

Tam is hat mat

---

5. Egg hen the with is this

egg the with is this hen.

The hen is with this egg.

6. egg chick a is in the

A chick is in the egg.

chick A egg in is the

Home Activity Your child learned to recognize sentences. Write groups of simple words that are sentences and groups of words that are not. Ask your child to identify the sentences and explain his or her choices.

1.1.D.1 Recognize distinguishing features of a sentence.

Name _____

Read the words in the box.
Pick a word to finish each sentence.
Write it on the line.

he	is	to	with	three

1. Basketball _____ fun.

2. The _____ squirrels are eating .

3. Sam likes to play _____ Pat.

4. We can go _____ the party Saturday.

5. When will _____ move to his new house?

1.3.H.1 Identify at least 100 high-frequency words from a commonly used list. **Also 1.3.H.2.**

Name _____

Vv

Say the word for each picture.
Write v on the line if the word has the same first sound as .

---

1. _____

2. _____

3. _____

4. _____

5. _____

6. _____

Write V or v to make a word.

7. _____ at

8. _____ ic

9. _____ al

10. _____ an

Home Activity Your child learned that some words begin with the letter v. Have your child find other words with /v/ as in *volcano*.

1.2.E.1 Isolate initial sounds in one-syllable spoken words. **Also 1.2.E.2, 1.2.F.1, 1.3.A.2.i.20.**

Name _____

Circle the make-believe pictures.
Draw a box around the real pictures.

1.

2.

3.

4.

5.

6.

Home Activity Your child looked at pictures to tell which may be real and which may be make-believe. With your child, look at a book about how real people and animals live.

🌐 **1.9** Make inferences about the structure and elements of fiction.

Name _____

Trace and **write** the letters. Make sure you write your letters the correct size.

V

V

Copy the words. Write the letters the correct size.

Val

Vin

vest

vast

vent

vat

van

Vic

Home Activity Your child practiced writing words with *Vv*. Have your child choose a word that begins with *V* and a word that begins with *v* from above, and practice writing each word two more times.

1.21.A.1 Form upper-case letters legibly in text, using the basic conventions of print (left-to-right and top-to-bottom progression), including spacing between words and sentences. **Also 1.21.A.2.**

Name _____

Read each group of words.
Find and **copy** the complete sentence.

1. The cat ran.
   is my hat
   had been to

   _____
   -
   _____

2. Kim can win.
   run Kim to see
   my van is a

   _____
   -
   _____

3. A big jet is.
   Pam can pat the cat.
   on mat we see cat on

   _____
   -
   _____

4. My top is in
   The lad is sad.
   Is sad the lad

   _____
   -
   _____

School + Home **Home Activity** Your child learned to recognize sentences and features such as capitalization and end punctuation. Have your child circle the capital letter in each sentence on this page.

🌎 **1.1.D.1** Recognize the distinguishing features of a sentence.

Name _____

Yy   Zz

Say the word for each picture.
Write y on the line if the word has the same first sound as .
Write z on the line if the word has the same first sound as 🦓.

1. ⃝ _____	2. _____
3. _____	4. _____
5. _____	6. _____
7. _____	8. _____

School + Home

Home Activity Your child learned that some words begin with y and some words begin with z. Have your child find other words that begin with /y/ as in yo-yo and /z/ as in zebra.

🌐 1.2.E.1 Isolate initial sounds in one-syllable spoken words.
Also 1.3.A.1.i.23, 1.3.A.2.i.23, 1.3.A.2.i.24.

Phonics Consonant *Yy/y/* and *Zz/z/*   **105**

Name _____

Sentences

A **sentence** tells a complete idea.
It begins with a capital letter.
Many sentences end with a period.

noun

↑

The wet dog runs.

↓   ↓

adjective   verb

Find the sentence.

Underline the sentence.

1. The girl will get the one with fuzz.

   the one with fuzz

2. the fun park

   They can go to the fun park.

3. Here is where they sell good fruit.

   good fruit

4. wet up here

   You can get wet up here.

5. I can see the big rainbow.

   big rainbow

School + Home

Home Activity Your child learned about expanding sentences. Say a simple sentence to your child and have him or her add a word to the sentence.

1.1.D.1 Recognize distinguishing features of a sentence.

Name _____

Trace and **write** the letters.
Make sure you write your letters
the correct size.

Y y   Z z

Y

y

Z

Z

Home Activity Your child practiced writing *Yy* and *Zz*. Have your child practice writing all four letters three more times each.

1.21.A.1 Form upper-case letters legibly in text, using the basic conventions of print (left-to-right and top-to-bottom progression), including spacing between words and sentences. **Also 1.21.A.2.**

Name _____

Read each group of words.
Find and **copy** the complete sentence.

1. pup Ned is a
   Ned and Ted
   Ned is a pup.

   _____
   -
   _____

2. a is dog this
   This dog is a
   This is a dog.

   _____
   -
   _____

3. Tim dog is for this
   This dog is for Tim.
   dog this Tim for is

   _____
   -
   _____

4. The dog nap and will Tim
   The dog and Tim nap.
   Tim nap dog The and will

   _____
   -
   _____

Home Activity Your child learned to recognize sentences and features such as end punctuation. Find sentences and other groups of words in a flyer, periodical, or used worksheet. Ask your child to identify the sentences and circle the end punctuation.

⊕ 1.1.D.1 Recognize the distinguishing features of a sentence.

Name _____

Uu

Say the name of the picture.

Write u on the line if the word has the same first sound as .

1.	2.
3.	4.

Say the name of the picture.

Write u on the line if the word has the same middle sound as .

5. s ___ n   6. t ___ b

7. b ___ g   8. p ___ n

School + Home

Home Activity Your child learned about the short *u* vowel sound in words. Have your child find other words that have the same sound as /u/ at the beginning or in the middle, such as *umbrella* and *rug*.

Name _____

Read the words in the box.

Pick a word to finish each sentence. **Write** it on the line.

Remember to begin a sentence with a capital letter.

where here for me go

1. The ⬭ is for _____ .

2. We are waiting _____ the rain to stop.

3. _____ can we buy pickles?

4. Let's _____ to the Farmers Market.

5. _____ are three yams.

Home Activity This week your child identified and read the words *where, here, for, me,* and *go.* As you read with your child, encourage him or her to point out these words in print.

1.3.H.1 Identify at least 100 high-frequency words from a commonly used list. **Also 1.3.H.2.**

Sentences

Tell about what you get at a store.
Use words from the box or words of your own.

food   toys   books   games

_____
- - - - - - - - - - - - - - - - - -
_____

_____
- - - - - - - - - - - - - - - - - -
_____

_____
- - - - - - - - - - - - - - - - - -
_____

_____
- - - - - - - - - - - - - - - - - -
_____

Say other sentences about things in a store.

Home Activity Your child learned how to expand sentences in writing. Have your child add adjectives to the sentences he or she wrote.

Name _____

Trace and **write** the letters. Make sure you write your letters the correct size.

U   u

↓U↓   _____

↓u↓   _____

Copy the words.

Uncle _____   junk _____

just _____   dull _____

hug _____   sun _____

Did you write each **U** and **u** the correct size?   Yes   No

Home Activity Your child practiced writing words with *Uu*. Read the following sentence to your child: *It is fun to run in the sun.* Have your child copy the sentence as neatly as he or she can.

🌟 **1.21.A.1** Form upper-case letters legibly in text, using the basic conventions of print (left-to-right and top-to-bottom progression), including spacing between words and sentences. **Also 1.21.A.2.**

Name _____

Read each group of words.
Find and **copy** the complete sentence.

1. pup sit and Tom
   The pup can sit.
   Tom the pup sit

   _____
   -
   _____

2. A pup can run.
   The fat pup fat on
   fat pup beg can

   _____
   -
   _____

Finish each sentence. **Write** a word and a [.]

   _____
   -
3. I like _____

   _____
   -
4. We see a _____

   _____
   -
5. Tom fed the _____

   _____
   -
6. Sam is with _____

   _____
   -
7. Tam can go _____

   _____
   -
8. Tip has a yellow _____

Home Activity Your child learned to recognize sentences and features such as capitalization and end punctuation, and then use these features to complete sentences. Point to sentences in a newspaper or magazine. Have your child identify the features of a sentence. Then have your child find complete sentences.

1.1.D.1 Recognize the distinguishing features of a sentence.

Print Awareness 113

Name _____

Qq

Say the word for each picture.
Write q on the line if the word has the same first sound as the picture.

1.	2.
3.	4.
5.	6.

Write qu to make a word.

7. _____ **ilt**

8. _____ **it**

9. _____ **iz**

10. _____ **ick**

School + Home

Home Activity Your child learned that some words begin with the letter *q*. Have your child find other words that begin with /kw/ as in *quilt*.

⊕ **1.2.D.1** Blend spoken phonemes to form one-syllable words, including consonant blends. **Also 1.2.E.1, 1.2.F.1, 1.3.A.2.i.15.**

Name _____

Read the story.
Look at each pair of pictures.
Circle the one that shows something real.

My class went to a museum.

Butterflies were flying around in a special room.

In another room, we learned about horses.

There were models and pictures of horses.

We saw the bones of a huge dinosaur.

That was my favorite part of the museum.

1.

2.

3.

4.

5.

6.

 School + Home **Home Activity** Your child read a story that could really happen. Then your child identified which of two pictures shows something real. Talk about a place you and your child have gone to, such as a zoo, park, or fair. Have your child name things that were real at that place.

🔹 **1.9** Understand the structure and elements of fiction.

Name _____

Sentences

Mark the word that completes the sentence.

1. Zak can _____ a big yam.
   - ○ girl
   - ○ fuzz
   - ○ sell

2. We go for a _____ run.
   - ○ Sam
   - ○ long
   - ○ quit

3. They can go here to get _____.
   - ○ mop
   - ○ run
   - ○ fruit

4. They can _____ up at the rainbow.
   - ○ look
   - ○ big
   - ○ zoo

 Home Activity Your child prepared for taking tests on expanding sentences. Name a family member and have your child say two sentences about that person. Tell your child to include a noun, a verb, and an adjective in each sentence.

1.1.D.1 Recognize distinguishing features of a sentence.

Name _____

1. **Circle** the shelf with .

2. **Draw** a box around the shelf with [📖📖📖] .

3. **Draw** an X over the computer.

4. **Draw** an arrow to the shelf with books of poems.

5. **Underline** the shelf with DVDs.

School + Home

Home Activity Your child learned to find resources in the library. Visit your local library with your child and help him or her find the storybooks, poems, newspapers, signs, and labels.

1.24 Locate and explore the full range of sources addressing a research question.

Research Using a Library/Media Center   **117**

Name _____

Trace and **write** the letters.
Make sure you write your letters
the correct size.

Q q   Q u

Q

q

Q u

q u

School + Home **Home Activity** Your child practiced writing *Qu* and *qu*. Have your child practice writing this sentence: *Quin quit his quest.*

118 **Handwriting**

1.21.A.1 Form upper-case letters legibly in text, using the basic conventions of print (left-to-right and top-to-bottom progression), including spacing between words and sentences. **Also 1.21.A.2.**

Name _____

Read each group of words.
Find and **copy** the complete sentence.

1. ham the Ben is for
    The ham is for Ben.
    Ben ham is the for

    _____

    _____

2. I see a big yam.
    A yam I see big
    See yam big I a

    _____

    _____

Finish each sentence. **Write** a word and a [.]

_____
----
3. Dad can _____

_____
----
4. The hat is _____

_____
----
5. They have to _____

_____
----
6. A cat is on _____

_____
----
7. Kit and Tip see _____

_____
----
8. I see a green _____

Home Activity Your child learned to recognize sentences and features such as capitalization and end punctuation, and then use these features to complete sentences. Read the sentences that your child completed. Discuss the features of each sentence. Ask if each sentence makes sense.

1.1.D.1 Recognize the distinguishing features of a sentence.

Print Awareness 119

Name _____

Read the words in the box.
Pick a word to finish each sentence.
Write it on the line.

where   here   for   me   go

1. Viv asked if Tim could come _____ for a visit.

2. The rainbow may _____ away.

3. I know _____ you live.

4. Bill can come with _____ to the game.

5. She bought vegetables _____ Jan.

Home Activity This week your child identified and read the words *where, here, for, me,* and *go.* As you read with your child, encourage him or her to point out these words in print.

1.3.H.1 Identify at least 100 high-frequency words from a commonly used list. **Also 1.3.H.2.**

Say the word for each picture.
Write a on the line if you hear the **short a** sound.

c<u>a</u>t

1.

b _____ g

2.

f _____ n

3.

m _____ p

4.

m _____ p

5.

c _____ n

6.

m _____ n

7.

p _____ g

8.

v _____ n

Write a word for each picture.

9.

_____

10.

_____

 School + Home **Home Activity** Your child has reviewed words with the short *a* sound heard in *cat*. Work with your child to make words that rhyme with *cat* and *man*.

1.3.B.1 Combine sounds from letters to create recognizable words. **Also 1.3.B.2.**

Phonics Short *a* **121**

Name _____

Read the words in the box.
Pick a word to finish each sentence.
Write it on the line.

| my | on | way | in | come |

1. We go that _____ to the .

2. The can _____ to me.

3. This is _____ .

4. The is _____ my .

5. The is _____ my .

© Pearson Education, Inc., 1

 Home Activity This week your child identified and read the words *in, on, my, way,* and *come.* Write each word on a card. Have your child read each word and then use it in a sentence.

122 High-Frequency Words

1.3.H.1 Identify at least 100 high-frequency words from a commonly used list. **Also 1.3.H.2.**

Name _____

Look at the pictures.

Circle a word to finish each sentence of the story.

1. Sam has a cat.
   The cat had a _____.   nap   tag

2. The cat ran.
   Sam is _____.   lap   sad

3. The cat is in the jam.
   Sam is _____.   bad   mad

4. The cat ran.
   The cat is _____.   bad   sad

Circle the picture to finish the sentence.

5. The story takes place in a _____.

Home Activity Your child identified characters' actions and feelings. Reread the story with your child. Talk about why Sam felt the way he did.

1.9.B.3 Describe reasons for characters' feelings.
Also 1.9.B.1, 1.9.B.2, 1.9.   **Comprehension** Character and Setting   **123**

Name _____

Writing • Story

 Pooky the Cat

Pooky is our cat. He is silly. He plays with everything.

Today, Mom dropped a pen. The pen fell on the floor.

Pooky ran to the pen. He hit the pen. The pen rolled across the floor. Pooky chased the pen. He hit it again. It rolled away.

"Silly Pooky!" said Mom. "He thinks the pen is a toy!"

Key Features of a Story

• The story has characters and tells what they do.

• It is made of sentences.

1.18.A.1 Write brief stories that include a beginning, middle, and end.

Name _____

Say the word for each picture.

Write ck on the line if the word has the same ending sound as .

1.

ta _____

2.

ba _____

3.

fa _____

4.

sa _____

5.

ha _____

6.

ja _____

7.

pa _____

8.

ca _____

Write two words that have the same ending sound as .

_____   _____

_____   _____

School + Home **Home Activity** Your child practiced reading and creating words that end in *ck*. Help your child write words that rhyme with *sack*.

🟢**1.3.B.1** Combine sounds from letters to create recognizable words. **Also 1.3.B.2, 1.3.A.2.iv.7.**

Phonics Final *ck* **125**

Name _____

Short *a* Words

Write two list words that rhyme with **pan**.

1. **c** _____

2. **r** _____

Spelling Words
at
can
cat
back
dad
am
bat
mad
ran
sack

Write two list words that rhyme with **sad**.

3. **m** _____

4. **d** _____

Write two list words that rhyme with **tack**.

5. **b** _____

6. **s** _____

Write two list words that rhyme with **hat**.

7. **c** _____

8. **b** _____

Write the missing words.   (am   at)

9. Look _____ me.   10. I _____ on a box.

Home Activity Your child wrote words with the short *a* vowel sound. Point to a picture on this page and have your child spell the word.

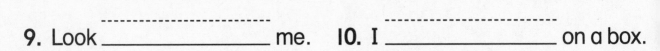

🌐 **1.22.A.1** Use phonological knowledge to match sounds to letters to construct words. **1.22.B.1.i** Use letter-sound patterns to spell consonant-vowel-consonant (CVC) words.

Sentences

A **sentence** is a group of words that tells a complete idea. It begins with a capital letter. Many sentences end with a period (.).

The cat is on a mat.   ← This is a sentence.
on a mat   ← This is not a sentence.

Find the sentence. **Write** the sentence.

1. Jim has a pet.   has a pet

_____
- -
_____

2. His pet   His pet is a cat.

_____
- -
_____

3. The cat   The cat runs away.

_____
- -
_____

4. Jim looks for his pet.   for his pet

_____
- -
_____

5. with Jim   We go with Jim.

_____
- -
_____

Home Activity Your child learned about sentences. Name an animal your child knows. Have your child say two sentences about the animal.

1.1.D.1 Recognize distinguishing features of a sentence.

Conventions Sentences **127**

Name _____

Story Chart

Title_____

```
┌─────────────────────────────────────┐
│ Characters                          │
│                                     │
│                                     │
│                                     │
└─────────────────────────────────────┘

┌─────────────────────────────────────┐
│ Beginning                           │
│                                     │
│                                     │
│                                     │
│                                     │
└─────────────────────────────────────┘
                   ↓
┌─────────────────────────────────────┐
│ Middle                              │
│                                     │
│                                     │
│                                     │
│                                     │
└─────────────────────────────────────┘
                   ↓
┌─────────────────────────────────────┐
│ End of Story                        │
│                                     │
│                                     │
│                                     │
└─────────────────────────────────────┘
```

© Pearson Education, Inc., 1

School + Home

Home Activity Your child is learning to write a little story. Ask your child what stories are like.

🌟 **1.18.A.1** Write brief stories that include a beginning, middle, and end.

Name _____

A   a

Copy the words. Write the letters the correct size.

Ann _____   nap _____

tap _____   ham _____

cap _____   ran _____

jab _____   yak _____

wag _____   sad _____

rag _____   pal _____

sat _____   Pam _____

Did you write all of your letters the correct size? | **Yes** | | **No** |

Home Activity Your child practiced writing words with *A* and *a* and the short *a* sound. Have your child draw a picture of two of the words he or she wrote and label the pictures with the words.

1.21.A.1 Form upper-case letters legibly in text, using the basic conventions of print (left-to-right and top-to-bottom progression), including spacing between words and sentences. **Also 1.21.A.2.**

Handwriting   **129**

Name _____

Read each question. Write the correct answer.

Best Foods for Cats and Dogs

A New Bed for Ted

A Vet for My Pet

a frog   a bird   a fish

1. Who is Ted? _____

in a nest   on the ground   in a chair

2. Where does Ted sleep? _____

3. Which book is about pet doctors?

_____

_____

4. Which book could help you learn about feeding your pet?

_____

_____

5. Other than books, where else could you look to learn more about birds?

_____

_____

School + Home

Home Activity Your child learned how to select books based on their titles or key words. Together with your child, make a list of topics you may enjoy reading about. Then, if possible, go to the library and choose some age-appropriate books based on your topics of interest.

1.24.B Use text features to locate information. **Also 1.23.B.1.**

Jack and Dad Pack

Short a		Final -ck	High-Frequency Words
at	cap	Jack	I
bag	Dad	back	said
and	had	sack	the
bat	hat	pack	look
can	map		
	ran		
	sat		
	van		

Jack and Dad sat.

"I can pack the bag," said Dad.

"I can pack the sack," said Jack.

Dad had the bag at the van.

Jack ran back!

Decodable Story *Jack and Dad Pack*
Target Skill Short a, Final -ck

1.3.A.1.ii.1 Decode words in context by applying common letter-sound correspondences, including: single letters (vowels) including short a. **Also 1.3.A.2.ii.1, 1.3.A.1.iv.7.**

"I can pack the hat."

"I can pack the map," said Dad.

"Look at the sack!" said Dad.

"I can pack the bat and cap," said Jack.

Short *a* Words

Find a list word to finish the sentence.
Write it on the line.

_____
1. The bug _____ hop.

_____
2. I _____ sad.

_____
3. His _____ has a van.

_____
4. The dog _____ .

_____
5. I _____ the ball.

_____
6. Look _____ the fox.

_____
7. I fed my _____ .

_____
8. Put the can in the _____ .

_____
9. I know the _____ to go.

_____
10. I want to _____ with you.

Spelling Words

at

can

cat

back

dad

am

bat

mad

ran

sack

High-Frequency Words

way

come

School + Home

Home Activity Your child wrote spelling words to complete sentences. Help your child make up a new sentence for each spelling word.

1.22.A.1 Use phonological knowledge to match sounds to letters to construct words. **1.22.B.1.i** Use letter-sound patterns to spell consonant-vowel-consonant (CVC) words. **Also 1.22.C.1.**

Spelling Short a Words **133**

Sentences

Tell a story about when you did something with a pet.
Use some words from the box in your sentences.

run play feed watch

_____
- -
_____

_____
- -
_____

_____
- -
_____

_____
- -
_____

_____
- -
_____

_____
- -
_____

Home Activity Your child learned how to use sentences in writing. Have your child write two sentences that tell about a pet your family has had.

✦ **1.1.D.1** Recognize distinguishing features of a sentence.

Name _____

Short *a* Words

Circle the word that names the picture.

Spelling Words
at
can
cat
back
dad
am
bat
mad
ran
sack

1.   sack
   can
   cat

2.   cat
   bat
   dad

3.   back
   sack
   bat

4. dad
   ran
   mad

5. can
   bat
   ran

6. can
   ran
   cat

Say the words. Circle the two words that are the same.
Write the word.

7. can   at   at   am   7. _____

8. back   sack   at   back   8. _____

9. ran   am   can   am   9. _____

10. ran   mad   mad   dad   10. _____

School + Home

Home Activity Your child has been learning to spell words with short *a*. To review what your child has learned, take turns thinking of and spelling simple words with short *a*.

1.22.A.1 Use phonological knowledge to match sounds to letters to construct words. 1.22.B.1.i Use letter-sound patterns to spell consonant-vowel-consonant (CVC) words.

Name _____

Sentences

Mark the group of words that is a sentence.

1. ○ Ron gets a pet today.
   ○ a pet today
   ○ gets a pet

2. ○ a big cat
   ○ The pet is a big cat.
   ○ the pet

3. ○ plays with his
   ○ with his cat
   ○ Ron plays with his cat.

4. ○ He rolls the ball to the cat.
   ○ ball to the cat
   ○ rolls the ball to

5. ○ hits the ball
   ○ the ball back
   ○ The cat hits the ball back.

6. ○ and the cat like
   ○ Ron and the cat like the game.
   ○ Ron and the cat

School + Home **Home Activity** Your child prepared for taking tests on sentences. Read a story together. Have your child point out sentences in the story.

✪ **1.1.D.1** Recognize distinguishing features of a sentence.

Name _____

Say the word for each picture.
Write i on the line if you hear the **short i** sound.

pig

1.

k _____ ck

2.

h _____ ll

3.

t _____ ck

4.

f _____ n

5.

p _____ n

6.

d _____ g

7.

w _____ g

8.

z _____ p

Circle the word to finish each sentence. **Write** it on the line.

9. _____

I _____ go.

will   wall

10. _____

Sam _____ the mat.

hip   hid

School + Home

Home Activity Your child practiced creating words with the short i sound heard in *pig*. Help your child make up fun rhymes using short i words, such as *The big pig in the wig can dig and do a jig.*

1.3.B.1 Combine sounds from letters to create recognizable words. Also 1.3.B.2.

Name _____

Read the words in the box. **Pick** a word to finish each sentence.
Write it on the line. **Remember** to use a capital
letter at the beginning of a sentence.

| up   take   she   what |

_____
- -
1. My cat is _____ .

_____
- -
2. You can _____ two.

_____
- -
3. _____ has a pack.

_____
- -
4. _____ can Nan fix?

Home Activity This week your child identified and read the words *up, take, she,* and *what*. As you read with
your child, encourage him or her to point out these words in print.

1.3.H.1 Identify at least 100 high-frequency words from a commonly
used list. **Also 1.3.H.2.**

Name _____

Read the story.

Circle the answer to each question about the story.

Jill and Meg play with a .

They hit the .

They pop the !

Jill and Meg are sad.

But Dad has a for them.

Jill and Meg play with the .

---

1. What happens first?

   Jill and Meg play with a .

   Jill and Meg are sad.

2. What happens that is sad?

   Jill and Meg kick the .

   Jill and Meg pop the .

3. What happens so Jill and Meg are not sad?

   Dad has a for Jill and Meg.

   Dad has a doll for Jill and Meg.

4. What happens last?

   Jill and Meg hit the .

   Jill and Meg play with the .

School + Home **Home Activity** Your child identified the plot, or what happens in a story, and the problem and solution in a story. Read a short fairy tale and have your child identify a problem and solution.

Name _____

Writing · Fantasy Story

 Wise Owl

One day, Janey visited her friend, Wise Owl. He was sad.

"The animals come to ask me questions," he said. "Now I
have a question. Whom should I ask?"

"I can help you," said Janey.

"I miss my brother and sister," Wise Owl said. "But my
brother lives in the east. My sister lives in the west. I do not
know where to go. What should I do?"

"Ask them to visit you!" said Janey.

Wise Owl smiled. "Thank you for your help," he said.

Key Features of a Fantasy Story

• Characters and events are made up.

• Characters do things that real people and
animals cannot do.

🌀 **1.18.A.1** Write brief stories that include a beginning, middle, and end.

Name _____

Say the word for each picture.
Write x on the line if the word has the same
ending sound as **ax**.

a<u>x</u>

1.

si _____

2.

wa _____

3.

li _____

4.

ki _____

5.

bo _____

6.

mi _____

7.

si _____

8.

fi _____

Write two words that have the same ending sound as **6**.

_____   _____
- - - - - - - - - - - - - - - - -   - - - - - - - - - - - - - - - - -
_____   _____

Read the sentence below. **Underline** the words that have the
same ending sound as **ax**.

He saw six wax cats.

Home Activity Your child practiced creating words that end with *x*. Write *six, mix,* and *fix* on cards. Have
your child choose a card, read the word, and use it in a sentence.

1.3.B.1 Combine sounds from letters to create recognizable
words. Also **1.3.A.1.i.22, 1.3.A.2.i.22, 1.3.B.2.**

Phonics Final *x*   **141**

Name _____

Short *i* Words
Write letters to finish the word.

Spelling Words
in
it
did
sit
six
fix
lip
mix
pin
wig

1. p _____   2. s _____

3. w _____   4. l _____

5. s _____   6. m _____

7. f _____   8. i _____

Write the missing words.   (it   did)

9. I hit _____.

10. Yes, I _____.

School + Home **Home Activity** Your child spelled words with the short *i* vowel sound. Point to a picture on this page and have your child spell the word.

142 **Spelling** Short *i* Words

⊕ **1.22.A.1** Use phonological knowledge to match sounds to letters to construct words. **1.22.B.1.i** Use letter-sound patterns to spell consonant-vowel-consonant (CVC) words.

Name _____

Subjects of Sentences

A sentence has a **naming part**. It names a person, place, animal, or thing. The naming part tells who or what the sentence is about.

Pat sees a pig.   **The pig** is big.

↑   ↑

naming part   naming part

Write the naming part of each sentence.

1. My pig is sick.

_____

- -

_____

2. A vet can help the pig.

_____

- -

_____

3. We go to the vet.

_____

- -

_____

4. The pig feels better.

_____

- -

_____

5. My dad thanks the vet.

_____

- -

_____

Home Activity Your child learned about the naming parts of sentences. Read a story together. Point to several sentences. Ask your child to identify the naming part of each sentence.

Name _____

Story Chart

Title _____

Characters

Beginning

Middle

End of Story

Home Activity Your child planned a story. Share a brief story, and have your child tell what happens at the beginning.

✪ **1.17.A** Plan a first draft by generating ideas for writing.

Name _____

Trace and **write** the letters. Make sure you
write your letters the correct size.

X

X

Copy the words. Leave the correct space between letters.

X-ray

pig

mix

six

Ina

rip

Did you leave the correct space between your letters? **Yes** **No**

Home Activity Your child practiced writing words with *Ii* and *Xx*. Have your child practice writing each of
these letters five more times.

⭐ **1.21.A.1** Form upper-case letters legibly in text, using the basic
conventions of print (left-to-right and top-to-bottom progression),
including spacing between words and sentences. **Also 1.21.A.2.**

Handwriting 145

Name _____

Read each question. **Circle** the correct answer.

1. What would you use to read a story about a frog?

2. What would you use to find the meaning of **vet**?

3. What would you use to find more about what vets do?

4. What would you use to find out what time the zoo opens?

5. What would you use to watch a show about animals?

 Home Activity Your child learned about sources that are available at a library or media center. Together with your child make a list of some of the sources found at a library. If possible, go to the library together and see how many of these sources you can find.

1.23.B.1 Decide what sources of information might be relevant to answer these questions.

Jill Can!

Short i				Consonant x /ks/	High-Frequency Words
pick	zip	fit	sit	six	is
quick	pin	win		fix	the
Jill	rip				with
will	lid				

Jill is six.

Jill can zip.

Jill can pin the rip.

1

Jill can pick the bat.

Jill is quick!

Jill will win.

Decodable Story *Jill Can!*
Target Skill Short *i*, Consonant *x*/ks/

1.3.A.1.ii.3 Decode words in context by applying common letter-sound correspondences, including: single letters (vowels) including short *i*. **Also 1.3.A.1.i.22, 1.3.A.2.i.22, 1.3.A.2.ii.3.**

4

Jill can fix the lid.
The lid will fit.

Jill can pat the cat.
The cat will sit with Jill.

Name _____

Short *i* Words

Spelling Words				
in	it	did	sit	six
fix	lip	mix	pin	wig

High-Frequency Words
she
take

Circle a word to finish the sentence. **Write** the word.

_____

1. He is   **fix**   **six**   **pin** .   _____

2. I bit my   **lip**   **did**   **sit** .   _____

3. Put   **sit**   **it**   **fix**   in the box.   _____

4. Can she   **in**   **wig**   **fix**   it?   _____

5. You can   **sit**   **lip**   **six**   here.   _____

6. His   **did**   **wig**   **in**   is red.   _____

7. They   **pin**   **six**   **did**   not go.   _____

8. Help me find a   **pin**   **sit**   **in** .   _____

9. I will   **did**   **pin**   **take**   the book.   _____

10. Can   **did**   **she**   **pin**   mix it?   _____

Home Activity Your child wrote spelling words to complete sentences. Read a sentence, say the spelling word, and ask your child to spell the word. Continue with other sentences.

1.22.A.1 Use phonological knowledge to match sounds to letters to construct words. 1.22.B.1.i Use letter-sound patterns to spell consonant-vowel-consonant (CVC) words. Also 1.22.C.1.

Spelling Short *i* Words   **149**

Name _____

Subjects of Sentences

Complete each sentence with a naming part.

1. _____ is my favorite color.

2. _____ is my favorite food.

3. _____ is my favorite day.

Tell about things you like to do. Write your sentences.

_____

_____

_____

_____

_____

_____

Home Activity Your child learned how to use naming parts of sentences in writing. Ask your child to underline the naming parts of the sentences he or she wrote on the page.

1.1.D.1 Recognize distinguishing features of a sentence.

Name _____

Short *i* Words

Write the missing letters. Then write the words.

1. [ ] [t]

_____
- - - - - - - - - - - - - - - - - - - -

2. [f] [ ] [ ]

_____
- - - - - - - - - - - - - - - - - - - -
_____

3. [ ] [n]

_____
- - - - - - - - - - - - - - - - - - - -
_____

4. [s] [ ] [x]

_____
- - - - - - - - - - - - - - - - - - - -

Spelling Words
in
it
did
sit
six
fix
lip
mix
pin
wig

Write a list word that rhymes with each word.

5. pig

_____
- - - - - - - - - - - - - - - - - - - -

6. hip

_____
- - - - - - - - - - - - - - - - - - - -

7. lid

_____
- - - - - - - - - - - - - - - - - - - -

8. tin

_____
- - - - - - - - - - - - - - - - - - - -

9. fit

_____
- - - - - - - - - - - - - - - - - - - -

10. six

_____
- - - - - - - - - - - - - - - - - - - -

Home Activity Your child has been learning to spell words with short *i*. To review, draw some circles. Have your child write a short *i* word in each circle.

1.22.A.1 Use phonological knowledge to match sounds to letters to construct words. **1.22.B.1.i** Use letter-sound patterns to spell consonant-vowel-consonant (CVC) words.

Name _____

Subjects of Sentences

Mark the sentence that has a line under the naming part.

1. ○ My mom <u>is</u> a vet.
   ○ <u>My mom</u> is a vet.
   ○ My mom is a <u>vet</u>.

2. ○ <u>She</u> helps sick animals.
   ○ She <u>helps</u> sick animals.
   ○ She helps <u>sick</u> animals.

3. ○ That dog cut <u>its</u> leg.
   ○ That dog <u>cut</u> its leg.
   ○ That <u>dog</u> cut its leg.

4. ○ <u>This cat</u> hurt its paw.
   ○ This cat hurt <u>its</u> paw.
   ○ This cat <u>hurt</u> its paw.

5. ○ A vet will fix <u>them</u>.
   ○ <u>A vet</u> will fix them.
   ○ A vet <u>will</u> fix them.

6. ○ The animals <u>like</u> my mom.
   ○ The animals like <u>my</u> mom.
   ○ <u>The animals</u> like my mom.

School + Home **Home Activity** Your child prepared for taking tests on the naming parts of sentences. Write simple sentences about your family, such as these: *Anne is your sister. Your mother works at a bank.* Ask your child to circle each naming part.

✪ **1.1.D.1** Recognize distinguishing features of a sentence.

Name _____

Say the word for each picture.
Circle the picture if the word has
the **short o** sound you hear in **top**.

<u>t**o**p</u>

1.

2.

3.

4.

5.

6.

7.

8.

9.

10.

11.

12.

13.

14.

15.

 School + Home

Home Activity Your child practiced creating words with the short *o* sound heard in *top*. Encourage your child to use the short *o* words pictured above in sentences.

1.3.B.1 Combine sounds from letters to create recognizable words.

Phonics Short *o* **153**

Name _____

Read the words in the box.
Pick a word to finish each sentence.
Write it on the line.

| blue | from | help | little | get | use |

1. Can I _____ your ?

2. I can take it _____ you.

3. I will _____ a .

4. My dogs _____ you go.

5. I see a big _____ ox!

6. The dogs are _____ .

1.3.H.1 Identify at least 100 high-frequency words from a commonly used list. **Also 1.3.H.2.**

© Pearson Education, Inc. 1

Name _____

Look at each pair of pictures.
Circle the pictures that show characters in settings that
make sense. **Think** about what they are doing.

I.

2.

3.

Draw a picture of a character from a story doing something.
Show how he or she feels.

4.

Home Activity Your child learned about characters and places in a story. As you read together, have your child tell you what he or she knows about the characters and settings in the stories.

1.9.B.1. Describe characters in a story. **Also** 1.9.B.2, 1.9.B.3.   **Comprehension** Character and Setting   **155**

Name _____

Writing · Short Poem

 Kitty

Kitty's eyes are big and green.

She stretches, yawns, and licks her paws clean.

Key Features of a Short Poem

· A short poem has words written in lines that
  may rhyme.

· It can describe something or can express
  feelings.

🔻**1.18.B.1** Write short poems that convey sensory details.

Name _____

Circle a word to match each picture.

pan**s**

1.

bat   bats

2.

mop   mops

3.

rock   rocks

4.

pig   pigs

5.

top   tops

6.

cap   caps

7.

kit   kits

8.

sack   sacks

Write a sentence for each word.

9. cats _____

_____

10. wigs _____

Home Activity Your child identified singular and plural nouns. Have your child name items around the house. Point out the use of -s at the end of many plural words, such as *books, apples,* and *bowls.*

1.3.A.2.i.18 Decode words in isolation by applying common letter-sound correspondences, including: single letters (consonants) including s=/z/.

Phonics -s Plurals   **157**

Name _____

Short *o* Words

Spelling Words				
Mom	hot	hop	pot	pop
ox	lock	mop	got	rock

Write a word that rhymes.

1. **sock** on a

_____

2. **hot**

_____

3. **box** on an

_____

4. **block** on a

_____

5. **top** by a

_____

6. **Tom** and

_____

Draw a line from the word to its shape.
Write the word in the shape.

hot

mop

pop

got

7.

8.

9.

10.

School + Home

Home Activity Your child spelled words with the short *o* vowel sound. Help your child spell each word and then think of a rhyming word.

158 **Spelling** Short *o* Words

🌐 **1.22.A.1** Use phonological knowledge to match sounds to letters to construct words. **1.22.B.1.i** Use letter-sound patterns to spell consonant-vowel-consonant (CVC) words.

Name _____

Predicates of Sentences

A sentence has an **action part.** It tells what a person or thing does.

The ox **helps.**   He **pulls the wagon.**

↑   ↑

action part   action part

Write the action part of each sentence.

1. The cow gives milk.

_____

- -

_____

2. Pop milks the cow.

_____

- -

_____

3. The hen lays eggs.

_____

- -

_____

4. Mom gets the eggs.

_____

- -

_____

5. The cat chases mice.

_____

- -

_____

 Home Activity Your child learned about the action parts of sentences. Read a story together. Point to several sentences. Ask your child to identify the action part of each sentence.

1.1.D.1 Recognize distinguishing features of a sentence.

Conventions Predicates of Sentences **159**

Name _____

Web

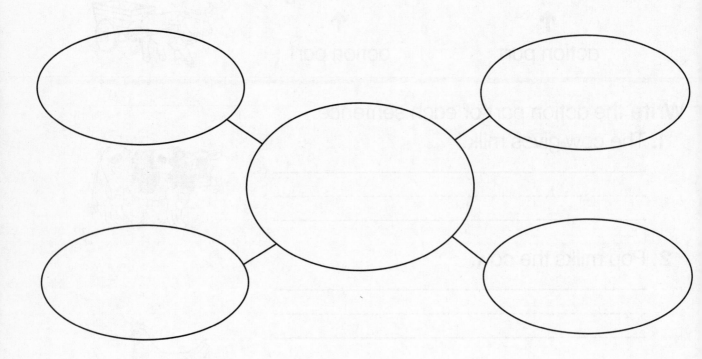

1.17.A.1 Plan a first draft by generating ideas for writing.

Name _____

Copy the words. Write the letters from left to right.

Oz

pot

box

mom

cob

doll

log

job

hot

not

got

sob

rod

fox

Did you write the letters from left to right?   Yes   No

 Home Activity Your child practiced writing words with *O* and *o* and the short *o* sound. Have your child choose two words from above and write the words three more times.

 1.21.A.1 Form upper-case letters legibly in text, using the basic conventions of print (left-to-right and top-to-bottom progression), including spacing between words and sentences. **Also 1.21.A.2.**

Handwriting   161

Name _____

How do animals help people?

1. **Use** the picture to think about a topic. **Write** two topic ideas.

_____

_____

_____

2. **Circle** your favorite topic.

3. **Think** about what else you want to know about your topic.
   Write three questions.

_____

_____

_____

_____

Home Activity Your child generated topic ideas for a picture and then formulated questions to research.
Discuss topics that your child is interested in and, if possible, look up information about one of the topics.

1.23.A.1 Generate a list of topics of class-wide interest.
Also 1.23.A.2.

What Is In the Box?

Short *o*		Plural -s + Consonant *s/z/*	High-Frequency Words	
box	not	rocks	are	go
fox	on	socks	in	is
got	top	**mops**	the	what
Dot				

Are rocks in the box?

Six rocks are in the box.

A fox is not in the box.

The fox is on top!

Decodable Story *What Is In the Box?*
Target Skills Skills Short *o*, Plural -s + Consonant *s/z/*

1.3.A.1.ii.4 Decode words in context by applying common letter-sound correspondences, including: single letters (vowels) including short *o*. **Also 1.3.A.1.i.18, 1.3.A.2.i.18, 1.3.A.2.ii.4.**

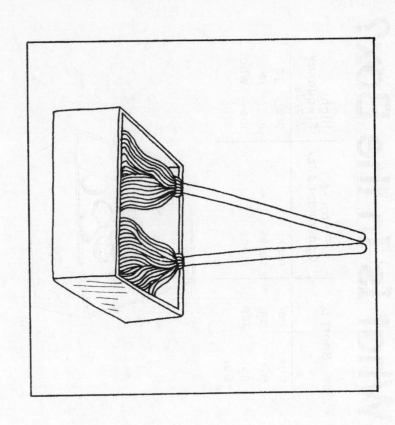

Are mops in the box?
The mops are in the box.

Dot got the socks.
The socks can go in the box.

Name _____

Short *o* Words

Find a list word to finish the sentence.
Write it on the line.

Spelling Words

mom
hot
hop
pot
pop
ox
lock
mop
got
rock

1. Fill the _____ .

2. She is my _____ .

3. I will _____ up the mess.

4. Frogs can _____ .

5. The sun is _____ .

6. He is my _____ .

7. Put a _____ on his van.

8. I _____ wet.

9. I will _____ my top.

10. Can you _____ me now?

High-Frequency Words

help
use

Home Activity Your child wrote spelling words to complete sentences. Have your child make up and write new sentences for several of the words.

1.22.A.1 Use phonological knowledge to match sounds to letters to construct words. 1.22.B.1.i Use letter-sound patterns to spell consonant-vowel-consonant (CVC) words. Also 1.22.C.1.

Name _____

Predicates of Sentences

Complete each sentence. **Write** an action part. **Tell** what the animal does.

1. A horse _____.

2. A duck _____.

3. A dog _____.

Tell about things that other animals do. **Use** words from the box or your own words. **Write** your sentences.

swims   jumps   hops   runs

_____

_____

_____

_____

Home Activity Your child learned how to use action parts of sentences in writing. Ask your child to underline the action parts of the sentences he or she wrote on the page.

1.1.D.1 Recognize distinguishing features of a sentence.

Name _____

Short *o* Words

Write the words in the puzzle.

Spelling Words

mom

hot

hop

pot

pop

ox

lock

mop

got

rock

Connect the matching hearts.

mom   mom

          got   pot   hot

hop

pop

got   pop   hot   pot

hop

School + Home **Home Activity** Your child has been learning to spell words with short *o*. Have your child think of and write words that rhyme with *spot* or *stop*.

1.22.A.1 Use phonological knowledge to match sounds to letters to construct words. **1.22.B.1.i** Use letter-sound patterns to spell consonant-vowel-consonant (CVC) words.

Name _____

Predicates of Sentences

Mark the sentence that has a line under the action part.

1. ○ Ox gets a mop.
   ○ Ox gets a mop.
   ○ Ox gets a mop.

2. ○ He mops the pigs.
   ○ He mops the pigs.
   ○ He mops the pigs.

3. ○ Mom and Pop ride on Ox.
   ○ Mom and Pop ride on Ox.
   ○ Mom and Pop ride on Ox.

4. ○ Ox gets the cans.
   ○ Ox gets the cans.
   ○ Ox gets the cans.

5. ○ He packs the sack.
   ○ He packs the sack.
   ○ He packs the sack.

6. ○ They take a nap.
   ○ They take a nap.
   ○ They take a nap.

Home Activity Your child prepared for taking tests on the action parts of sentences. Write simple sentences about your family, such as these: *Bill plays football. Your sister feeds the baby.* Ask your child to circle each action part.

168 Conventions Predicates of Sentences

✪ **1.1.D.1** Recognize distinguishing features of a sentence.

Name _____

Add -s to each word.
Write the new word on the line.

1. hop _____

2. sit _____

3. see _____

4. pat _____

5. help _____

Use the words you wrote to finish the sentences.
Write the words on the lines.

6. Jack _____ a big dog.

7. Jack _____ the dog.

8. Jack _____ on a rock.

9. The dog _____ Jack.

10. The dog _____ on Jack.

School + Home **Home Activity** Your child added -s to verbs. Have your child write the verbs *see, fan, nap, dig, sit, hop, jog,* and *mop*, and add an -s to each verb. Have your child pick a verb and use it in a sentence about you, such as *Mommy hops*. Then act out the sentence.

1.3.E.1 Read base words with inflectional endings.

Phonics Inflected Ending *-s* **169**

Name _____

Read the words in the box.

Pick a word to finish each sentence.

Write it on the line. **Remember** to begin a sentence with a capital letter.

eat	four	five	her	this	too

1. We see _____
_____

2. The _____
_____

3. _____
_____ is a big cat.

4. This is a big cat _____
_____ .

5. Can we help _____
_____ ?

6. We see _____
_____ .

Home Activity This week your child identified and read the words *eat, four, five, her, too,* and *this*. Look through books to find these words in print and have your child read them aloud.

1.3.H.1 Identify at least 100 high-frequency words from a commonly used list. **Also 1.3.H.2.**

Name _____

Read each story.
Circle the sentence that tells best what the story is about.
Underline a detail that tells about the main idea.
Then **write** the topic of the story.

---

1. Dan has a cat.

   The cat is tan.

   The cat is fat.

   Dan has a fat, tan cat.

2. Topic:

   _____

   _____

   cat   mop

---

3. Whales are big animals.

   Whales have big tails.

   Whales have big fins.

   Whales eat a lot.

4. Topic:

   _____

   _____

   fins   whales

Write the name of a story you have read.
Draw a picture that shows what the story is about.

_____

5. _____

Home Activity Your child learned about the main idea and details of a story. As you read stories together, have your child tell you the main idea.

Name _____

Writing · Personal Narrative

 The Loon

Last summer my family camped next to a lake. I liked waking up outside. Then I swam all day long!

One morning my dad took me to the lake. "Look!" he said. I saw a beautiful black bird floating on the lake.

"It is a loon," Dad said. "Loons can stay underwater a long time. They can dive deep and swim far. Watch!"

The loon dived underwater. We watched and waited. A minute later, we saw the loon again. I was amazed! It was so far away. We could hardly see it.

"If the loon comes again tomorrow, let's use our binoculars to watch," Dad said. I couldn't wait!

Key Features of a Personal Narrative

· The narrative tells a story about a real event in the author's life.

· It tells how the author feels about the event or gives the author's opinion.

🌀 **1.18.A.1** Write brief stories that include a beginning, middle, and end.

Name _____

Add -ing to each word.
Write the new word on the line.

1. help _____

2. look _____

3. fix _____

4. lick _____

5. play _____

Use the words you wrote to finish the sentences.
Write the words on the lines.

6. Jan is _____ at the cats.

7. Jan is _____ the cats.

8. The cats are _____ with the can.

9. The big cat is _____ the little cat.

10. Jan is _____ the lock.

Home Activity Your child added -ing to verbs. Have your child write the verbs lick, rock, kick, eat, and mix on slips of paper. Then have your child add -ing to each verb. Have your child pick a slip of paper and act out the word for you to guess.

🌐 **1.3.E.1** Read base words with inflectional endings. **Also 1.3.B.2.**

Name _____

Inflected Ending -s

Write list words to finish the sentences.

1. They _____ .   2. It _____ .

3. They _____ .   4. He _____ .

5. They _____ in bed.   6. He _____ in bed.

7. They _____ on mats. 8. She _____ on a mat.

9. They _____ the race. 10. He _____ the race.

 Home Activity Your child spelled pairs of words with and without the -s ending. Point to a word on this page and have your child spell the other word in the pair.

✦ **1.22.A.1** Use phonological knowledge to match sounds to letters to construct words. **1.22.D.1** Spell base words with inflectional endings.

Declarative Sentences

A **telling sentence** tells something. It is a **declarative sentence**.
It begins with a **capital letter**. It usually ends with a **period (.)**.

The fox has a kit.
The kit naps.

Find the sentence. **Underline** the sentence.

1. The children see a fox.

   the children see a fox

2. they see the kit

   They see the kit.

3. The kit can run.

   the kit can run

4. the fox and kit play

   The fox and kit play.

5. fox naps on the rocks

   Fox naps on the rocks.

Home Activity Your child learned about telling sentences. Read a story together. Have your child point to sentences in the story and name the capital letter at the beginning and the period at the end.

1.21.C.1 Recognize punctuation marks at the end of declarative sentences.
1.21.C.4 Use punctuation marks at the end of declarative sentences.

Conventions Declarative Sentences   **175**

Name _____

Story Chart

Title _____

Beginning

Middle

End of Story

School + Home **Home Activity** Your child can plan to write about real events. Share a memory about an event such as a time you saw animals at a zoo.

✪ **1.17.B.1** Develop drafts by sequencing ideas through writing sentences.

Name _____

Nn   Gg

Copy the words. Slant all of the letters the same way.

Gus _____   acting _____

Nan _____   fixing _____

singing _____   mixing _____

Gil _____   bumping _____

ringing _____   telling _____

adding _____   packing _____

passing _____   kicking _____

Do all of your letters slant the same way? | Yes | | No |

Home Activity Your child practiced writing words with *Nn* and *Gg* and words ending in *-ing*. Name a word from the chart, point to it, and have your child copy it on a separate sheet of paper. Continue with other words.

1.21.A.1 Form upper-case letters legibly in text, using the basic conventions of print (left-to-right and top-to-bottom progression), including spacing between words and sentences. **Also 1.21.A.2.**

Name _____

Look at the chart. **Answer** the questions.

Adult Animals	Baby Animals
bear	cub
deer	fawn
elephant	calf

1. The topic of Lee's report is "Animals." Will this chart help?

    _____

    _____

2. Is there enough information in the chart for Lee to write about "Animals"?

    _____

    _____

3. Lee wants to revise his topic. Use Lee's chart to choose the topic.

    Animals and Their Babies

    Big Animals

4. Why is that a better topic for Lee?

    _____

    _____

Home Activity Your child learned how review and revise a topic. Ask your child to choose a topic that is of interest to him or her. Have him or her list some facts about the topic. Then using a reference source, read about the topic and ask your child to revise the facts based on your research.

1.25.A.1 Revise the topic (with adult assistance) as a result of answers to initial research questions.

Name _____

Circle the word for each picture.

we**b**

1.

mitt   men   man

2.

bed   bid   bad

3.

pen   pan   pin

4. **10**

tin   tan   ten

5.

jam   jet   jog

6.

net   not   nip

Circle the word the completes each sentence.

7. The fat _____ sits on my lap.

hen   hat

8. I like my short _____ hat.

rid   red

School + Home

Home Activity Your child practiced reading words with the short *e* sound heard in *web*. Work with your child to make words that rhyme with *pet* or *bell*.

Name _____

Read the words in the box.
Pick a word to finish each sentence.
Write it on the line. **Remember** to use a capital letter at the beginning of a sentence.

saw	small	tree	your

_____
- -
1. We _____ a tree.

_____
- -
2. It was not a big _____.

_____
- -
3. Do you like this _____ tree?

_____
- -
4. _____ tree is not wet.

Home Activity This week your child identified and read the words *saw, small, tree,* and *your.* Make flashcards with one word on each card. Mix them up and have your child read the words.

186   High-Frequency Words

1.3.H.1 Identify at least 100 high-frequency words from a commonly used list. **Also** 1.3.H.2.

Name _____

Read each story.
Circle the sentence that tells best what the story is about.
Underline a detail that tells about the main idea.
Then **follow** the directions.

I. Ben has a hen.

The hen is red.

The hen is fat.

Ben has a fat, red hen.

2. What is the topic of the story? **Write.**

_____

- - - - - - - - - - - - - - - - - -

_____

red   hen

---

3. Kim is a kid.

Brad is a kid.

Kim likes to play.

Brad likes to play.

Kim and Brad like to play.

4. **Write** your own main idea for the story.

_____

- -

_____

- -

_____

---

5. The bird has a nest in the tree.

The bird is big.

The nest is small.

The tree is tall.

6. **Write** your own main idea for the story.

_____

- -

_____

- -

_____

Home Activity Your child learned about the main idea and details of a story. As you read stories together, have your child tell you the main idea, or the most important point of the story.

1.13.A.1 Identify the topic of the text. **Also** 1.14.B.1, 1.14.B.2.

Name _____

Writing · Realistic Story

Little Squirrels

Luis and Lisa were playing at Lisa's house. They were running around and around.

"You are just like little squirrels!" Lisa's mom said. "The house is not for running! Go outside!"

Luis and Lisa went outside. "Why did your mom say that we are like squirrels?" Luis asked.

There was a big oak tree in the yard. Luis and Lisa sat under it. They watched the squirrels. The squirrels ran up the tree. The squirrels ran down the tree.

"Maybe we are like squirrels because we run so much!" Lisa said.

Key Features of a Realistic Story

• The characters, events, and setting seem real.

• Characters do things that really can happen.

1.18.A.1 Write brief stories that include a beginning, middle, and end.

Name _____

Pick letters from the box to finish each word.
Write the letters on the line.

 swim

```
bl  cl  cr  dr  fl  fr  gr  sl  sm  st
```

1. _____ ag

2. _____ ock

3. _____ ap

4. _____ ess

5. _____ ab

6. _____ og

7. _____ ell

8. _____ ed

9. _____ ep

10. _____ in

School + Home

Home Activity Your child practiced creating words with initial blends *(flag, dress, sled)*. Help your child make up silly sentences that each contain words beginning with just one blend, such as *Freddy frog likes French fries.*

1.3.B.1 Combine sounds from letters to create recognizable words. **Also 1.3.B.2.**

Phonics Initial Blends   **189**

Name _____

Short e Words

Spelling Words				
bed	men	red	step	ten
net	leg	jet	sled	wet

Write three list words that rhyme with **pet.**

1. _____ 2. _____ 3. _____

Write three list words that rhyme with **Ted.**

4. _____ 5. _____ 6. _____

Write the missing word.

7. Let's make two _____ out of snow.

8. We need _____ buttons.

9. Do not _____ on his hat.

10. Does he need a _____ ?

| leg |
| step |
| men |
| ten |

Home Activity Your child spelled words with the short *e* vowel sound. Have your child draw and label some of the words.

1.22.A.1 Use phonological knowledge to match sounds to letters to construct words. **1.22.B.1.i** Use letter-sound patterns to spell consonant-vowel-consonant (CVC) words.

© Pearson Education, Inc. 1

Name _____

Interrogative Sentences

A **question** is an asking sentence. It is an **interrogative sentence.**
It begins with a **capital letter.** It ends with a **question mark (?).**

What will we see**?**
Is that a nest**?**

Put a ✓ by each question.

1. Who lives in the nest? _____

   A bird lives in the nest. _____

2. The big bird is red. _____

   Is the big bird red? _____

3. Can the big bird help? _____

   The big bird can help. _____

4. I can get the eggs. _____

   Can you get the eggs? _____

5. Where is the egg? _____

   The egg is in the nest. _____

School + Home

Home Activity Your child learned about questions. Read a story together. Have your child find any questions in the story and name the capital letter at the beginning and the punctuation mark at the end.

1.21.C.3 Recognize punctuation marks at the end of interrogative sentences.

Conventions Interrogative Sentences **191**

Name _____

Story Chart

Title_____

Characters

Setting

Beginning

Middle

End of Story

Home Activity Your child is learning about realistic stories. Have him or her describe a real place.

192 **Writing** Plan

1.17.A.1 Plan a first draft by generating ideas for writing.

Name _____

E -------- e

Copy the words. Write the letters the correct size.

Emma _____   red _____

set _____   ten _____

leg _____   vest _____

bed _____   hen _____

fell _____   jet _____

net _____   den _____

hem _____   get _____

Did you write all of your letters the correct size? | Yes | No |

Home Activity Your child practiced writing words with *E* and *e* and the short *e* sound. Have your child write as many words with *E* or *e* that he or she can think of that are not on this page. You can use the words from above to help your child write rhyming words.

 1.21.A.1 Form upper-case letters legibly in text, using the basic conventions of print (left-to-right and top-to-bottom progression), including spacing between words and sentences. **Also 1.21.A.2.**

Name _____

Look at the lists.
Follow the directions and **answer** the questions.

Wild Animals	Pets
bear	cat
fox	dog
frog	fish
lion	frog
tiger	hamster

1. **Think** of two more wild animals. **Write** the animal names.

_____ _____

_____ _____

2. **Think** of two more pets. **Write** the animal names.

_____ _____

_____ _____

3. **Circle** the animal that you would like to know more about.
   Share your choice with the class.

4. **Think** about what else you want to know about your animal.
   Write two questions.

_____

_____

_____

Home Activity Your child learned how to identify topics and ask questions about a topic. Ask your child to make up another question about one of the topics above.

1.23.A.1 Generate a list of topics of class-wide interest. **Also** 1.23.A.2.

The Blocks

Short e		Initial consonant blends	High Frequency Words
Meg	bed	blocks	the
gets	fell	black	a
ten	Peg	step	up
red	mess	stack	help
sets	yells		

Meg gets ten blocks.

Meg has red blocks.

Meg has black blocks.

"Pick up the blocks," Mom yells.

"Peg will help!"

4

Decodable Story *The Blocks*
Target Skills Short e, Initial consonant blends

1.3.A.1.ii.2 Decode words in context by applying common letter-sound correspondences, including: single letters (vowels) including short e. **Also 1.3.A2.ii.2, 1.3.A.1.iii.**

Meg sets the blocks on the step.

Meg will stack the blocks on the bed.

The blocks fell.

Peg got Mom.

"Meg has a mess!"

Name _____

Short e Words

Spelling Words
bed   men   red   step   ten   net   leg   jet   sled   wet

Choose a word to finish the sentence.
Fill in the circle. **Write** the word.

1. I made the ◯ bed ◯ men ◯ leg .

2. Do not get me ◯ step ◯ wet ◯ net !

3. Her sock was ◯ sled ◯ jet ◯ red .

4. Kick with your ◯ ten ◯ net ◯ leg .

5. Kim has a ◯ red ◯ sled ◯ wet .

6. A fish is in the ◯ net ◯ ten ◯ step .

7. Sit on the ◯ ten ◯ step ◯ red .

8. I will count to ◯ ten ◯ jet ◯ sled .

Write the words and complete the sentence.

9. I _____ _____ sled.

High-Frequency Words
saw
your

School + Home

Home Activity Your child wrote spelling words to complete sentences. Help your child find other spelling words that make sense in the sentences. For example, sentence 1 could read "I made the **net**."

1.22.A.1 Use phonological knowledge to match sounds to letters to construct words. **1.22.B.1.i** Use letter-sound patterns to spell consonant-vowel-consonant (CVC) words. **Also 1.22.C.1.**

Name _____

Interrogative Sentences

Finish the question. **Write** an animal name.

a bird

a cat

a dog

an elephant

an ostrich

What does _____ look like?

Read the sentence. **Change** the words to make a question.
Write the question.

The bird is red.

_____

_____

_____

_____

Home Activity Your child learned how to use questions when writing. Say a sentence about one of the animals on the page, such as *The elephant is big*. Have your child write your sentence as a question: *Is the elephant big?*

✪ **1.20.C.1** Ask questions with appropriate subject-verb inversion.
1.21.C.3 Recognize punctuation marks at the end of interrogative sentences.
1.21.C.6 Use punctuation marks at the end of interrogative sentences.

Name _____

Short e Words

Write the words.

Spelling Words
bed
men
red
step
ten
net
leg
jet
sled
wet

1. _____   2. _____

3. _____   4. _____

Circle the word that matches. **Write** it.

5. **bed**   bed   red   _____

6. **men**   wet   men   _____

7. **ten**   net   ten   _____

8. **sled**   step   sled   _____

9. **red**   red   sled   _____

10. **wet**   net   wet   _____

School + Home

Home Activity Your child has been learning to spell words with short *e*. Have your child think of and write words that rhyme with *set* or *fed*.

✪ **1.22.A.1** Use phonological knowledge to match sounds to letters to construct words. **1.22.B.1.i** Use letter-sound patterns to spell consonant-vowel-consonant (CVC) words.

Spelling Short e Words   **199**

Name _____

Interrogative Sentences

Find the question. **Mark** the question.

1. ○ The nest big is.
   ○ is the nest big?
   ○ Is the nest big?

2. ○ Do birds live here?
   ○ Birds do live here.
   ○ do birds live here?

3. ○ can you see the nest?
   ○ You can see the nest.
   ○ Can you see the nest?

4. ○ The big twig hit the nest.
   ○ Will the big twig hit the nest?
   ○ will the big twig hit the nest?

5. ○ are the birds in the nest?
   ○ Are the birds in the nest?
   ○ The birds in the nest are.

6. ○ Do you see eggs in the nest?
   ○ do you see eggs in the nest?
   ○ You do see eggs in the nest.

Home Activity Your child prepared for taking tests on questions. Together listen to a conversation or an interview on TV. Each time your child hears a question, have him or her say "Question!"

1.21.C.3 Recognize punctuation marks at the end of interrogative sentences.

Name _____

Say the word for each picture.
Write u on the line if you hear the **short u** sound.

p<u>u</u>p

1. b ____ g

2. d ____ ck

3. b ____ s

4. h ____ g

5. b ____ x

6. dr ____ m

7. s ____ n

8. sl ____ d

Write a sentence for each word.

9. mud _____

10. plum _____

School + Home

Home Activity Your child identified and created words with the short *u* sound heard in *pup*. Work with your child to write words that rhyme with *rug*.

1.3.A.ii Decode words in context and in isolation by applying common letter-sound correspondences, including single letters (vowels).

Phonics Short *u* 201

Name _____

Read the words in the box.
Pick a word to finish each sentence.
Write it on the line.

| home   into   many   them |

1. This is a _____ for 🐰 .

2. We see _____ 🐰 .

3. Do you see _____ ?

4. The 🐰 go _____ the home.

Draw a picture of you going into your home.

5.

Home Activity Your child identified and read the words *home, into, many,* and *them*. Invite your child to use the words to describe life in his or her home.

1.3.H.1 Identify at least 100 high-frequency words from a commonly used list. **Also 1.3.H.2.**

Name _____

Look at the picture that shows what happened.
Circle the picture that shows why it happened.

I.

2.

3.

Read the two story sentences. **Circle** the one that tells what happens.

4. Val is tan.   The pup ran.

5. Sam is sick.   Sam naps in bed.

Home Activity Your child learned about cause (why something happens) and effect (what happens). Look for cause and effect with your child. For example, you might point out that when the temperature drops in the fall, frost forms.

RC-1.D.2 Use textual evidence to support understanding.
Also RC-1.D.1.

Comprehension Cause and Effect   **203**

Name _____

Writing Prompt: Write a composition about an animal you like.

 Rabbits

I like rabbits. My mom and I watch rabbits in our yard. We see them in the evening. They eat and play at night. They rest during the day.

Rabbits eat plants. We try to keep them away from our garden.

Rabbits stand very still. They do not want us to see them! If I go too near to a rabbit, it hops away.

I learn a lot by watching rabbits.

1.19.A.1 Write brief compositions about topics of interest to the student.

Name _____

Say the word for each picture.
Circle the letters that finish each word.
Write the letters on the line.

ne**st**

---

nd   nt

_____
- - - - - - - - - - - - - -

1. po _____

nt   mp

_____
- - - - - - - - - - - - - -

2. ju _____

---

mp   nt

_____
- - - - - - - - - - - - - -

3. de _____

st   nt

_____
- - - - - - - - - - - - - -

4. ca _____

---

st   mp

_____
- - - - - - - - - - - - - -

5. la _____

nt   nd

_____
- - - - - - - - - - - - - -

6. ha _____

---

st   nt

_____
- - - - - - - - - - - - - -

7. ve _____

nt   mp

_____
- - - - - - - - - - - - - -

8. te _____

---

nt   st

_____
- - - - - - - - - - - - - -

9. fi _____

mp   st

_____
- - - - - - - - - - - - - -

10. sta _____

School + Home

Home Activity Your child created words using final consonant blends such as *mp, nd, nt,* and *st*. Have your child make up sentences using words from this page.

1.3.B.1 Combine sounds from letters to create recognizable words.
Also 1.3.B.2.

Name _____

Short *u* Words with Final Consonant Blends

Spelling Words				
just	dust	must	hunt	crust
bump	jump	trust	lump	dusk

Write a list word to name the picture.

I. _____ 2. _____ 3. _____

Read the clue. **Write** the list word.

4. It starts with **j**. It rhymes with **must**.

5. It starts with **d**. It rhymes with **husk**.

6. It starts with **h**. It rhymes with **stunt**.

7. It starts with **m**. It rhymes with **just**.

8. It starts with **d**. It rhymes with **bust**.

9. It starts with **tr**. It rhymes with **dust**.

10. It starts with **b**. It rhymes with **pump**.

School + Home

Home Activity Your child wrote words with the short *u* vowel sound. Take turns with your child making up clues and then guessing and spelling the word.

1.22.A.1 Use phonological knowledge to match sounds to letters to construct words. **1.22.B.1.iii** Use letter-sound patterns to spell one-syllable words with consonant blends.

Name _____

Exclamatory Sentences

An **exclamatory sentence** is a sentence that shows strong feeling. It begins with a **capital letter**. It ends with an **exclamation mark (!)**.

The animal is big!

Underline each sentence that is an exclamation.

1. That hippo is funny!

2. It looks mad!

3. Where does it live?

4. It can live in the mud.

5. Now the hippo is happy!

6. I like the hippo.

School + Home

Home Activity Your child learned about exclamations. Have your child read each exclamation on this page with strong feeling. Then take turns with your child saying exclamations of your own.

Name _____

Composition
Top-Score Response

Focus/Ideas	A good composition tells about one topic.
Organization	A good composition tells important ideas in an order that makes sense.
Voice	A good composition tells about the topic in a way that is interesting.
Word Choice	A good composition uses clear words.
Sentences	A good composition is written in complete sentences.
Conventions	A good composition has sentences that are punctuated correctly.

Home Activity Your child can begin to learn about writing on writing tests. Ask how writing a composition about a topic such as real animals is different from making up a story.

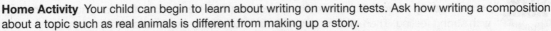 **1.17.B** Use elements of the writing process to compose text.

Name _____

Q q   U u

Copy the words. Leave the correct space between each letter.

Quin _____   tub _____

Uta _____   sun _____

quick _____   quiz _____

bus _____   duck _____

quit _____   hug _____

fun _____   mug _____

quack _____   jug _____

Did you leave the correct space between each letter? | Yes | | No |

Home Activity Your child practiced writing words with *Qq* and *Uu* and words with short *u* sound. Have your child copy this sentence as neatly as possible: *Quin and Uta quickly run to the bus.*

1.21.A.1 Form upper-case letters legibly in text, using the basic conventions of print (left-to-right and top-to-bottom progression), including spacing between words and sentences. **Also 1.21.A.2.**

Name _____

Use the picture to choose and revise a topic.

1. **Name** three animals you see. **Circle** the animal you would like to know more about.

2. What more would you like to know about this animal? **Write** two questions.

_____
- -
_____
- -
_____

3. Use your questions. **Write** your new topic. Ask for help if needed.

_____
- -
_____

Home Activity Your child learned how to answer questions about a topic. Encourage your child to ask questions about the topic "Preparing a Family Meal." After the questions are answered, ask your child if he or she wants to reword the topic.

1.25.A.1 Revise the topic (with adult assistance) as a result of answers to initial research questions.

The Test

Short u		Final Consonant Blends		High-Frequency Words	
Huff	fun	test	must	the	said
Bud	stuck	best		a	is
sum	sums				

"The class will get a test," said Miss Huff.

"The class will add."

Bud got the sums.

Bud did his best.

Bud did well!

4

Decodable Story The Test
Target Skills Short *u*, Final Consonant Blends

1.3.A.1.ii.5 Decode words in context by applying common letter-sound correspondences, including: single letters (vowels) including short *u*. **Also 1.3.A.1.iii, 1.3.H.2.**

1 + 1. Bud gets the sum.

3 + 3. The sum is six.

The test is fun!

5 + 5. Bud is stuck.

Bud must get the sum.

The sum is ten.

Name _____

Short *u* Words with Final Consonant Blends

Spelling Words

just	dust	must	hunt	crust
bump	jump	trust	lump	dusk

Write a list word to name the picture.

_____

1. It is _____ .

_____

2. I see the _____ .

_____

3. I _____ you.

_____

4. I _____ want to run.

_____

5. I _____ for an egg.

_____

6. Mom eats a _____ .

_____

7. I _____ into the car.

_____

8. My arm has a_____ .

_____

9. The car hits a _____ .

_____

10. We _____ go on the bus.

School + Home

Home Activity Your child wrote spelling words to complete a story. Help your child use some of the words in a story about his or her day.

★ **1.22.A.1** Use phonological knowledge to match sounds to letters to construct words. **1.22.B.1.iii** Use letter-sound patterns to spell one-syllable words with consonant blends.

Name _____

Exclamatory Sentences

What animal would you like to have?

Write about the animal.

Use an exclamation to show how you felt.

a zebra   an elephant   a lion   an ostrich   a hippo

Read the question. **Change** the words to make an exclamation.

Write the exclamation.

Is the pet big?

School + Home

Home Activity Your child learned how to use exclamations in writing. Name an object in the room and a word that describes the object *(lamp/bright; sofa/big; pillow/soft; rug/dark)*. Have your child write exclamations using the word pairs *(The lamp is too bright! That pillow is so soft!)*.

🟊 **1.20.C.1** Ask questions with appropriate subject-verb inversion.
1.21.C.2 Recognize punctuation marks at the end of exclamatory sentences.
1.21.C.5 Use punctuation marks at the end of exclamatory sentences.

Name _____

Short *u* Words with Final Consonant Blends

Write the words in the puzzle.

Spelling Words

Spelling Words
just
bump
dust
jump
must
trust
hunt
lump
crust
dusk

Write the missing words.

> bump   dusk   must   just

5. Do not _____ it.   6. I _____ get the ball.

7. I _____ want to play.   8. It is _____ now.

Home Activity Your child has been learning to spell words with short *u*. Help your child find words with short *u* in library books or schoolbooks.

1.22.A.1 Use phonological knowledge to match sounds to letters to construct words. **1.22.B.1.iii** Use letter-sound patterns to spell one-syllable words with consonant blends.

Spelling Short *u* Words with Final Consonant Blends   **215**

Exclamatory Sentences

Mark the correct exclamation.

1. ○ the big bird cannot fly!
    ○ The big bird cannot fly!
    ○ The big bird cannot fly

2. ○ The bird is so big!
    ○ The bird is so big
    ○ the bird is so big!

3. ○ the zebra loves the park!
    ○ The zebra loves the park
    ○ The zebra loves the park!

4. ○ Look at the big hippo!
    ○ Look at the big hippo
    ○ Look at the big hippo?

5. ○ The zebra is fast
    ○ The zebra is fast!
    ○ the zebra is fast

6. ○ Oh no, the bird fell
    ○ oh no, the bird fell!
    ○ Oh no, the bird fell!

Home Activity Your child prepared for taking tests on exclamations. Together read a favorite book. Have your child point out the exclamations and tell how he or she knew they were exclamations.

1.21.C.2 Recognize punctuation marks at the end of exclamatory sentences.

Name _____

Say the word for each picture.
Write sh or **th** to finish each word.

di<u>sh</u>   <u>th</u>ink

1.

_____
_ _ _ _ _ _ _ _
_____ op

2.

_____
_ _ _ _ _ _ _ _
fi _____

3.

_____
_____ in

4.

_____
_____ ell

5.

_____
_ _ _ _ _ _ _ _
ba _____

6.

_____
_ _ _ _ _ _ _ _
bru _____

Circle a word to finish each sentence. **Write** the word.

path   math

_____
_ _ _ _ _ _ _ _ _

7. She walked on the bike _____.

drip   ship

_____
_ _ _ _ _ _ _ _ _

8. I saw the _____ from the beach.

Home Activity Your child added the digraphs *sh* and *th* (two letters that together stand for one sound) to complete words. Have your child copy the words that contain *sh* from this page and use as many of those words as possible in one sentence. Repeat using the *th* words.

✪ **1.3.A.1.iv.3** Decode words in context by applying common letter-sound correspondences, including: consonant digraphs including *sh*. Also 1.3.A.1.iv.4, 1.3.A.2.iv.3, 1.3.A.2.iv.4.

Name _____

Read the words in the box.
Pick a word from the box to finish each sentence.
Write it on the line.

> catch   good   no   put   said   want

1. Dad and Bob _____ to fish.

2. "You can _____ it here," Dad said.

3. "I will," _____ Bob.

4. Bob has _____ fish yet.

5. Bob can _____ that fish!

6. It is a _____ fish.

Home Activity Your child identified and read the words *catch, good, no, put, said,* and *want.* As you read with your child, encourage him or her to point out these words in print.

1.3.H.1 Identify at least 100 high-frequency words from a commonly used list.   **Also 1.3.H.2.**

Name _____

Read the story.
Follow the directions.

Ted sees a nest fall from a tree.

It has three blue eggs in it.

Ted picks up the nest.

Ted sets the nest back in the tree.

1. **Write** a sentence that tells what happens at the beginning of the story.

_____

_____

_____

2. **Write** a sentence that tells what happens in the middle of the story.

_____

_____

3. **Draw** a picture that shows what happens at the end of the story. Then **act out** what happened in the story.

Home Activity Your child learned about the order in which things happen in a story. Reread this story with your child. Ask your child to tell you what might happen next in the story.

1.9 Understand the structure and elements of fiction.
Also 1.9.A.2., RC-1.E.2.

Comprehension Sequence **219**

Name _____

Writing • Friendly Letter

Dear Uncle Karl,

My favorite thing is fishing. I want you to go with me. We can go to the pond down the road. Then we will catch a bunch of fish. It will be really exciting! I hope you can go with me.

Your niece,

Lynn

Key Features of a Friendly Letter

• It begins with a greeting and ends with a closing.

• It often tells how the writer feels or gives the writer's opinion.

• It can tell ideas in time order, or sequence.

1.19.B Write short letters that put ideas in chronological or logical sequence and use appropriate conventions (e.g., date, salutation, closing).

Name _____

Circle a word to finish each sentence.
Write it on the line.

 b**a**ll

---

mall   mill

_____
- -
1. We met Dad at the _____.

---

well   walk

_____
- -
2. We take a _____ and talk.

---

tell   tall

_____
- -
3. Dad got a _____ bag.

---

all   ill

_____
- -
4. We _____ go in.

---

smell   small

_____
- -
5. I am too _____ to see!

School + Home

Home Activity Your child practiced reading words with the vowel sound heard in *ball* and *walk*. Work with your child to write a list of words that rhyme with *ball*.

Name _____

Words with *sh, th*

Spelling Words				
ship	fish	then	shut	with
rush	shell	shop	trash	thin

Find a list word to name the picture. **Write** it.

1. _____   2. _____   3. _____

4. _____   5. _____   6. _____

Unscramble the word. **Write** the word.

s	h	u	r

i	t	h	w

7. _____   8. _____

n	e	t	h

n	t	h	i

9. _____   10. _____

 Home Activity Your child wrote words with the *sh* or *th* sound. Say a list word. Ask if it has *sh* or *th*. Have your child spell the word.

1.22.A.1 Use phonological knowledge to match sounds to letters to construct words.

Common Nouns

A **noun** names a person, a place, an animal, or a thing.

The word **man** names a person.

The word **park** names a place.

The word **fish** names an animal.

The word **net** names a thing.

Write the noun for each picture. **Say** a sentence for each noun.

Person	**Place**
girl boy	city pond

1. _____

2. _____

Animal	**Thing**
cat rabbit	box pan

3. _____

4. _____

Home Activity Your child learned about nouns. Read a story together. Have your child point to nouns in the story and tell whether they name people, places, animals, or things.

1.20.A.2.iii Understand and use nouns (common) in the context of reading, writing, and speaking.

Conventions Common Nouns   **223**

Name _____

Letter Format

Dear _____ ,

_____
- -
_____

_____
- -

_____
- -

_____

_____
- -

_____
- -

_____
- -

                              _____
                              - - - - - - - - - - - - - - -
                              _____ ,
                              - - - - - - - - - - - - - - -
                              _____

Home Activity Your child is learning about writing letters. Help him or her plan a letter to a relative or family friend.

1.17.A Plan a first draft by generating ideas for writing. **Also 1.19.B.1.**

Name _____

S s   H h

Copy the words. Write the letters the correct size.

Shem _____   shack _____

Hal _____   dish _____

shop _____   rash _____

fish _____   mush _____

wish _____   cash _____

shut _____   Hank _____

ship _____   rush _____

Did you write all of your letters the correct size? | Yes | | No |

Home Activity Your child practiced writing words with *Ss* and *Hh* and short vowels. Have your child choose two words from the chart and write the words three more times.

1.21.A.1 Form upper-case letters legibly in text, using the basic conventions of print (left-to-right and top-to-bottom progression), including spacing between words and sentences. **Also 1.21.A.2.**

Name _____

See the USA

Contents

Welcome to the USA 5
Our Nation's Capital 11
National Parks 15
Historical Sites 19
Big Cities 23
Rural America 27
Sports Tour 35
Beaches, Beaches, Beaches 39
Natural Wonders. 43
Man-Made Fun 47

Use this **table of contents** from a travel book to find information.

1. **Draw** a circle around the page numbers.

2. **Put** a box around the chapter titles.

3. **Write** the name of the last chapter.

_____

_____

4. **Write** the page number on which the chapter "Beaches, Beaches, Beaches" begins.

_____

_____

5. **Write** the total number of chapters in *See the USA*.

_____

_____

Home Activity Your child learned to use the table of contents in a storybook to find information. As you read together, point out the table of contents and encourage your child to help you find information such as the page number for a specific chapter.

226 **Research** Parts of a Book

1.24.B.1 Use text features in age-appropriate reference works to locate information.

Cans

Consonant Digraphs	Vowel Sound in *ball* and *walk*	High-Frequency Words
cash	all	she
Smith	walk	the
with	talks	to
then		do
shed		
trash		
crush		
smash		

Miss Smith has cans.

She will not fill the trash with cans.

Miss Smith talks with Ned.

"Do not fill the land with trash!"

Decodable Story Cans
Target Skills Consonant Digraphs, Vowel Sound in *ball* and *walk*

1.3.A.2.iv.3 Decode words in isolation by applying common letter-sound correspondences, including: consonant digraphs including *sh*. **Also 1.3.A.1.iv.4, 1.3.H.2.**

Miss Smith will walk to the shed.

She will crush and smash the cans.

Miss Smith will fill all the bins with cans.

Then she will get cash.

Name _____

Words with *sh, th*

Find a list word or high-frequency word to finish the sentence.
Write it on the line.

1. I will _____ home.

2. Will you feed my _____ ?

3. Come _____ me.

4. Dad did a _____ job.

5. Put the paper in the _____ can.

6. This egg has a brown _____ .

7. Do not _____ the door.

8. I _____ to buy a new cap.

9. She came on a _____ .

10. That dog is _____ .

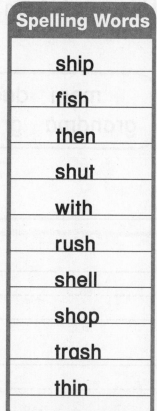

Spelling Words

ship
fish
then
shut
with
rush
shell
shop
trash
thin

High-Frequency Words

want
good

Home Activity Your child wrote spelling words and high-frequency words to complete sentences. Ask your child to write a sentence using two or more of the words.

1.22.A.1 Use phonological knowledge to match sounds to letters to construct words. **1.22.C.1** Spell high-frequency words from a commonly used list.

Spelling Words with *sh, th* **229**

Common Nouns

Write about things you do with your family.
Use words from the box or words of your own.

> mom   dad   brother
> grandma   grandpa   sister

_____

_____

- -

_____

- -

_____

- -

_____

- -

Choose other nouns. **Say** a sentence for each noun.

Home Activity Your child learned how to use nouns in writing. Write sentences about family members, such as *Your sister has brown hair. Your mother loves flowers.* Have your child circle the nouns in the sentences.

1.20.A.2.iii Understand and use nouns (common) in the context of reading, writing, and speaking.

Name _____

Words with *sh, th*

Read the clue. **Write** a list word.

It rhymes with ▱

_____

1. _____

It rhymes with

_____

2. _____

It rhymes with ⬭

_____

3. _____

It rhymes with 👧

_____

4. _____

Find a list word in each row of letters.
Circle it. **Write** it.

r u s h t e   5. _____

t s h u t r   6. _____

s h o p t h   7. _____

s t r a s h   8. _____

w i f i s h   9. _____

r w i t h s   10. _____

fish
shut
trash
rush
shop
with

Home Activity Your child has been learning to spell words with *sh* and *th*. Have your child circle *sh* and *th* in the spelling words.

1.22.A.1 Use phonological knowledge to match sounds to letters to construct words.

Spelling Words with *sh, th* **231**

Common Nouns

Mark the noun that completes the sentence.

1. Max wants a ____.
   - ○ eat
   - ○ fish
   - ○ will

2. The ____ has a pond.
   - ○ in
   - ○ sit
   - ○ park

3. Max got a red ____.
   - ○ ball
   - ○ talk
   - ○ this

4. A ____ is in the net.
   - ○ call
   - ○ and
   - ○ shell

5. The ____ gave them a fish.
   - ○ fat
   - ○ woman
   - ○ that

Home Activity Your child prepared for taking tests on nouns. Together read a simple piece of mail, such as an ad. Have your child circle the nouns in the article.

1.20.A.2.iii Understand and use nouns (common) in the context of reading, writing, and speaking.

Name _____

Circle the word for each picture.

c<u>a</u>ke

I.

rake   rack

2.

snack   snake

3.

frog   frame

4.

can   cane

5.

cape   cap

6.

plane   plan

Choose a word to finish each sentence. **Write** the word on the line.

lake   lock
----

7. I like to swim in the _____.

plant   plate
----

8. Please put the food on the _____.

gum   game
----

9. Will you play this _____ with me?

gate   skate
----

10. I can _____ fast.

School + Home

Home Activity Your child practiced reading words with the long *a* sound spelled *a _ e*, such as *cake*. Work with your child to write a list of words that rhyme with *cake*. Repeat with *cave*.

1.3.A.2.ii.6 Decode words in isolation by applying common letter-sound correspondences, including: single letters (vowels) including long *a* (*a-e*). **Also 1.3.B.2.**

Phonics Long *a*   **233**

Name _____

Read the words in the box.
Pick a word to finish each sentence.
Write it on the line.

be	could	horse	of	old	paper

1. Dad gave me a _____ .

2. She was not _____ .

3. She _____ run and jump.

4. I put her name on a _____ .

5. I can make the horse the color _____ a fox.

6. We will _____ pals!

School + Home **Home Activity** Your child identified and read the words *be, of, could, horse, old,* and *paper*. Write these words on small pieces of paper or self-stick notes. Tape them on a mirror or desk for your child to practice every day.

1.3.H.1 Identify at least 100 high-frequency words from a commonly used list. **Also 1.3.H.2.**

Name _____

Look at the first picture that shows what happened.
Circle the picture that shows why it happened.

Look at the picture that shows what happened.
Draw a picture that shows why it happened.

School + Home **Home Activity** Your child learned about cause (why something happens) and effect (what happens). Call your child's attention to causes and effects by asking questions such as: *What happened?* (effect) *Why did it happen?* (cause)

Name _____

Writing · Brief Composition

 Group Time

Every day we have group time. I work with José and Kim. We help each other with math. Sometimes we change papers. We talk about stories. We answer questions. Then we share with the class.

Key Features of a Brief Composition

· It tells interesting facts.

· It tells about one topic.

⊕ **1.19.A.1** Write brief compositions about topics of interest to the student.

Name _____

Circle the word for each picture.
Write it on the line.

 la**c**e a**g**e

1.

face   fake

_____
- - - - - - - - - - - -
_____

2.

rake   race

_____
- - - - - - - - - - - -
_____

3.

cave   cage

_____
- - - - - - - - - - - -
_____

4.

wag   wage

_____
- - - - - - - - - - - -
_____

5.

speck   space

_____
- - - - - - - - - - - -
_____

6.

stage   stake

_____
- - - - - - - - - - - -
_____

7.

track   trace

_____
- - - - - - - - - - - -
_____

8.

pace   page

_____
- - - - - - - - - - - -
_____

Circle the word to finish each sentence. **Write** the word.

lace   brake

_____
- - - - - - - - - - - - - - - - - - - -

9. I tripped on my _____ .

page   cage

_____
- - - - - - - - - - - - - - - - - - - -

10. My pet bird lives in a _____ .

 School + Home **Home Activity** Your child practiced reading and writing words that have the sound that c stands for in *lace* and the sound that g stands for in *age*. Ask your child to write a list of words that rhyme with *lace* and a list of words that rhyme with *age*.

Name _____

Words with Long *a*

Spelling Words				
face	made	age	safe	take
make	cage	cake	late	name

Write three list words that rhyme with **rake**.

1. _____ 2. _____ 3. _____

Write two list words that rhyme with **page**.

4. _____ 5. _____

Write the missing word.

> safe   face   name   late   made

6. Her _____ is Bo.

7. Bo _____ a dog.

8. Her _____ is happy.

9. Is that ball _____ ?

10. Can we stay _____ ?

Home Activity Your child wrote words with the long *a* sound. Help your child think of words that rhyme with the spelling words.

✪ **1.22.B.1.ii** Use letter-sound patterns to spell consonant-vowel-consonant-silent *e* (CVC*e*) words.

Name _____

Proper Nouns

Special names for people, places, animals, and things are called **proper nouns.** Proper nouns begin with capital letters.

Meg

Rose Pond

Rex

Tell Tower

Look at each picture. **Write** the proper name on the line.
Say a sentence for each proper noun.

Beth

1. This girl is _____.

Hall School

2. Beth goes to _____.

Post Road

3. The school is on _____.

Coco

4. The class pet is _____.

School + Home **Home Activity** Your child learned about proper nouns. Read a story together. Have your child point to proper nouns in the story.

1.20.A.2.iv Understand and use nouns (proper) in the context of reading, writing, and speaking. **Also 1.21.B.2.ii, 1.21.B.1.iii.**

Name _____

Idea Web

 School + Home

Home Activity Your child has thought of ideas for writing about how children work together. Share ideas about how people do things together at home.

1.17.A Plan a first draft by generating ideas for writing.

Name _____

P _____ p _____

Copy the words. Leave the correct space between the letters.

Page _____   wage _____

pace _____   lace _____

pave _____   race _____

tape _____   shade _____

cape _____   pale _____

cage _____   pane _____

face _____   rage _____

Did you leave the correct space between your letters? | Yes | | No |

Home Activity Your child practiced writing words with *P* and *p*. Have your child find two pairs of rhyming words in the list above and write the words two more times as neatly as possible.

 1.21.A.1 Form upper-case letters legibly in text, using the basic conventions of print (left-to-right and top-to-bottom progression), including spacing between words and sentences. **Also 1.21.A.2.**

Name _____

custodian – a person who helps keep buildings clean and safe

librarian – a person trained to work in a library

teacher – a person who helps people learn

1. Circle the school helper you would like to know more about.

2. What would you like to know? Write three interview questions.

_____

_____

_____

_____

_____

_____

3. Ask your interview questions. Write one thing you learned.

_____

_____

_____

4. Then act out your interview to share your results with the class.

Home Activity Your child learned how to interview. Have your child make a list of family members or friends that he or she would like to interview. Help your child come up with some interesting questions for the interview.

1.24.A.2. Gather evidence from interviews with local experts. Also 1.24.A.1, 1.26.A.1.

The Race

Long a: a_e		Consonants c /s/ and g /j/		High-Frequency Words	
Jake	gate	lane	race	pace	I	see
lake	late	shape	place	the	is
cake	skates	shade	age	of	for
takes	waves	Page
ate	came

Jake waves at Page. "I am in shape!"

"I will win the race at the lake."

Jake takes the fast lane.

See Jake dash past the gate.

Jake is fast for his age!

Decodable Story *The Race*
Target Skills Long *a: a_e*, Consonants *c /s/*, *g /j/*

1.3.A.1.i.3 Decode words in context by applying common letter-sound correspondences, including: single letters (consonants) including *c = /s/*. **Also 1.3.A.1.i.7, 1.3.A.1.ii.6, 1.3.H.2.**

Page waves at Jake.

"I came late. I ate lots of cake.

I will get last place."

Page walks in the shade.

She is not fast.

"I wish I had skates!"

Name _____

Words with Long *a*

Spelling Words					High-Frequency Words
face	made	age	safe	take	could
make	cage	cake	late	name	old

Circle a word to finish the sentence. **Write** the word.

_____

1. I love   **cake   late   make**!   _____

----

2. Have a   **face   safe   name**   trip.   _____

----

3. I   **made   age   cake**   it.   _____

----

4. What is your   **made   late   name**?   _____

----

5. His   **age   face   make**   got red.   _____

----

6. What is in the   **cage   age   face**?   _____

----

7. She won't tell her   **cake   late   age**.   _____

----

8. Let's   **safe   made   make**   a kite.   _____

----

9. I   **could cage   cake**   stay up late.   _____

----

10. That is an   **age   old   take   cage**.   _____

School + Home

Home Activity Your child used spelling words to complete sentences. Have your child identify and write as many spelling words as possible to finish this sentence: *This is my_____* .

✈ **1.22.B.1.ii** Use letter-sound patterns to spell consonant-vowel-consonant-silent *e* (CVC*e*) words. **1.22.C.1** Spell high-frequency words from a commonly used list.

Name _____

Proper Nouns

Finish each sentence with a proper noun.

_____

My teacher is _____.
(name of your teacher)

_____

My school is _____.
(name of your school)

Write the names of three children in your class.

_____   _____   _____

_____   _____   _____

Tell something about each child.

_____

_____

_____

_____

_____

Home Activity Your child learned how to use proper nouns in writing. Write sentences about people that you and your child know, such as *Steve is a friend. Maria is our cousin.* Have your child circle the proper nouns in the sentences.

1.20.A.2.iv Understand and use nouns (proper) in the context of reading, writing, and speaking. **Also 1.21.B.2.ii, 1.21.B.1.iii.**

Name _____

Words with Long *a*

Spelling Words				
face	made	age	safe	take
make	cage	cake	late	name

Use this code. **Write** the words.

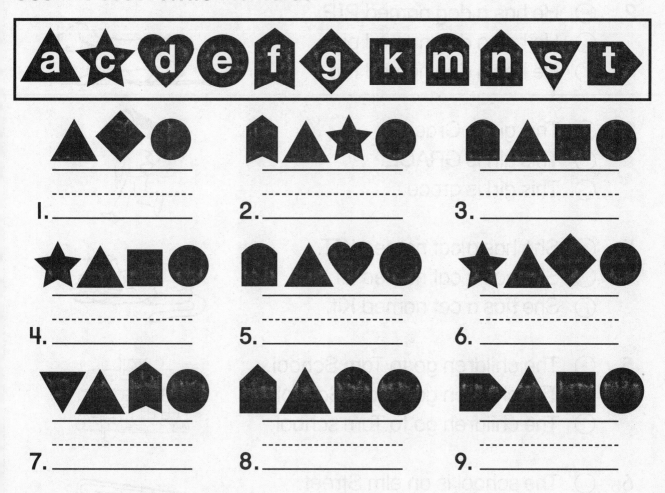

1. _____

2. _____

3. _____

4. _____

5. _____

6. _____

7. _____

8. _____

9. _____

Write the missing letters. **Write** the word.

10. l __ __ t   _____

School + Home

Home Activity Your child has been learning to spell words with long *a*. Ask your child to explain how all the list words are alike. (All have long *a*, and all end in *a*-consonant-e.)

1.22.B.1.ii Use letter-sound patterns to spell consonant-vowel-consonant-silent *e* (CVCe) words.

Proper Nouns

Mark the sentence that uses the proper noun correctly.

1. ○ This boy is jake.
   ○ This boy is Jake.
   ○ This boy is JAKE.

2. ○ He has a dog named PIP.
   ○ He has a dog named pip.
   ○ He has a dog named Pip.

3. ○ This girl is Grace.
   ○ This girl is GRACE.
   ○ This girl is grace.

4. ○ She has a cat named KIT.
   ○ She has a cat named kit.
   ○ She has a cat named Kit.

5. ○ The children go to Tam School.
   ○ The children go to tam School.
   ○ The children go to Tam school.

6. ○ The school is on elm Street.
   ○ The school is on Elm Street.
   ○ The school is on Elm street.

 Home Activity Your child prepared for taking tests on proper nouns. Together read a short newspaper or magazine article. Have your child circle the proper nouns in the article.

1.20.A.2.iv Understand and use nouns (proper) in the context of reading, writing, and speaking. **Also 1.21.B.2.ii, 1.21.B.1.iii.**

Name _____

Circle the word for each picture.

9 **nine**

1.	2.	3.	4.
vine vane	mane mice	wig wipe	bike bill

Say the name of each picture.
Write the letters to finish each word.

5.	6.	7.	8.
____ ____	____ ____	____ ____	____ ____

Pick a word to finish each sentence. Write the word on the line.

slice   price

_____

9. I bought a _____ of pizza.

bite   rice

_____

10. "Would you like a _____?" I asked.

1.3.A.2.ii.8 Decode words in context and in isolation by applying common letter-sound correspondences, including: single letters (vowels) including long *i* (*i_e*).

Name _____

Read the words in the box.

Pick a word to finish each sentence.

Write it on the line. **Remember** to use capital letters at the beginning of a sentence.

> live   out   people   who   work

1. _____ can fix this clock?

2. The _____ in the shop can fix it.

3. They will _____ on it.

4. Where does your dog _____ ?

5. His home is _____ here.

Home Activity Your child identified and read the words *live, out, people, who,* and *work.* Point to these words on the page. Have your child read each word and use it in a spoken sentence.

250   High-Frequency Words

1.3.H.1 Identify at least 100 high-frequency words from a commonly used list.   **Also 1.3.H.2.**

Name _____

Look at this book.
Write or **circle** your answers.

_____

_____

Who Works
at the Zoo?

by Kim Green

1. Who is the author of this book? _____

2. What is the topic of this book?

   people in the ocean   people at the zoo   people on a ship

3. Why do you think Kim wrote this book?

   to make you laugh   to teach you tricks   to tell facts

Draw a picture that shows what this book is about.

4.
┌───┐
│   │
│   │
│   │
│   │
│   │
│   │
│   │
│   │
│   │
└───┘

Home Activity Your child learned to tell what a book might be about by figuring out why it was written. As you read various materials with your child, ask what he or she thinks each is about and why the author wrote it.

1.13.A.2 Explain the author's purpose in writing about the text.
Also 1.13.A.1.

Comprehension Author's Purpose   **251**

Name _____

Writing • Explanation

 My Piano Teacher

Ms. Kindler teaches me to play piano. She shows me how to hold my fingers. She helps me read notes. She shows me the keys to press. She teaches me to play songs on the piano.

Key Features of an Explanation

- It tells about a person, idea, or thing.
- It helps people understand the topic.

1.19.A.1 Write brief compositions about topics of interest to the student.

Name _____

Circle the word for each picture.

 wh**isk**   **ch**ick   i**tch**

1.	2.	3.	4.
wall whale	shin chin	catch cats	wash watch

5.	6.	7.	8.
ship whip	chick check	patch pass	limp chimp

Pick a word to finish each sentence. **Write** the word on the line.

graph   grass

_____

9. Henry made a mistake on his _____ .

what   want

_____

10. He did not know _____ to do.

 School + Home   **Home Activity** Your child practiced reading words with digraphs *wh, ch,* and *tch* (letters that together stand for one sound). Have your child use each word above in a sentence.

1.3.A.2.iv.1 Decode words in isolation by applying common letter-sound correspondences, including: consonant digraphs including *ch*. Also 1.3.A.2.iv.2, 1.3.A.2.iv.5.

Name _____

Words with Long *i*

Spelling Words				
like	ride	smile	time	white
bike	dime	hide	ice	kite

Read the sentence. **Write** the words that rhyme.

They like the bike.

1. _____   2. _____

The kite is white.

3. _____   4. _____

Dad will use a dime this time.

5. _____   6. _____

Write the missing word.

7. The _____ makes me cold.

8. Did you walk or _____ ?

9. She has a big _____ on her face.

10. The cat likes to _____ from me.

ice
hide
ride
smile

School + Home **Home Activity** Your child wrote words with the long *i* sound. Take turns with your child making up sentences containing the words. Spell the words aloud.

1.22.B.1.ii Use letter-sound patterns to spell consonant-vowel-consonant-silent *e* (CVC*e*) words.

Name _____

Special Titles

A title can come before the name of a person. A title begins with a capital letter. Titles can be abbreviations. Abbreviations end with a period (.).

Doctor Silva   **Mrs.** Faber   **Mr.** Gray

Write the title and the name correctly on the line.

1. miss oda

_____
- -
_____

2. captain bartz

_____
- -
_____

3. dr. hashmi

_____
- -
_____

4. ms. ford

_____
- -
_____

© Pearson Education, Inc., 1

 School + Home **Home Activity** Your child learned about special titles. Say the names and titles of adults your child knows, for example, *Dr. Kahn, Ms. Bell, Mr. Garcia.* Ask your child to identify and write the person's title.

1.20.A.2.iv Understand and use nouns (proper) in the context of reading, writing, and speaking.

Name _____

Idea Web

1.17.A.1 Plan a first draft by generating ideas for writing.

Name _____

W

W

Copy the words. Write the letters from left to right.

Wade _____

chop _____

white _____

when _____

chime _____

whim _____

whine _____

chill _____

chin _____

which _____

while _____

whale _____

chase _____

Will _____

Did you write your letters from left to right? | Yes | | No |

School + Home

Home Activity Your child practiced writing words with *Ww*, *wh* and *ch*. Have your child choose three words from above and write the words one more time.

1.21.A.1 Form upper-case letters legibly in text, using the basic conventions of print (left-to-right and top-to-bottom progression), including spacing between words and sentences. **Also 1.21.A.2.**

Handwriting 257

Name _____

Look at the map.

1. **Circle** the school.

2. **Draw** a box around the bank.

3. **Underline** the park.

4. **Write** the number of houses on block C.

_____

- - - - - - - - - - - - - - - - - - -

_____

5. **Write** the number of cars on the map.

_____

- - - - - - - - - - - - - - - - - - -

Home Activity Your child learned to use a map to gather information. Point out maps as you see them and challenge your child to point out places featured on the maps.

🟊 1.15.B.2 Explain the meaning of specific symbols.

The White Kite

Long i: i_e		Consonant Digraphs wh, ch, tch, ph	High-Frequency Words
kite	nice	white	the
quite	line	checks	I
mile	dives	patch	a
smiles	like	Ralph	is
			go

Ralph calls Ann on the cell.

"I made a white kite!"

1

Ralph lets the kite go up.

It dips and dives.

"I like this kite!" Ralph tells Ann.

4

Decodable Story *The White Kite*
Target Skill Long *i: i_e*, Consonant Digraphs *wh, ch, tch, ph*

1.3.A.2.ii.8 Decode words in context and in isolation by applying common letter-sound correspondences, including: single letters (vowels) including long *i* (*i_e*). **Also 1.3.A.1.iv.1, 1.3.A.1.iv.2, 1.3.A.1.iv.5, 1.3.A.1.iv.10, 1.3.H.2.**

Ann checks the kite.

"It is small. But it is quite nice!"

Ralph smiles.

"The kite has a patch and a line.

It will go up a mile!"

Name _____

Words with Long *i*

Spelling Words				
like	ride	smile	time	white
bike	dime	hide	ice	kite

High-Frequency Words
who
work

Choose a word to finish the sentence.
Fill in the circle. **Write** the word.

1. The glass is full of ○ **ice** ○ **bike** ○ **dime**. _____

2. Be at ○ **who** ○ **smile** ○ **work** on time. _____

3. Look at the ○ **kite** ○ **hide** ○ **like**! _____

4. It costs a ○ **white** ○ **dime** ○ **ice**. _____

5. ○ **Work** ○ **Bike** ○ **Who** is coming? _____

6. You can ride my ○ **bike** ○ **ice** ○ **time**. _____

Read the word. **Write** the list word that means the opposite.

7. black _____   8. show _____

9. walk _____   10. frown _____

Home Activity Your child used spelling words and high-frequency words to complete sentences. Have your child identify and write as many spelling words as possible to finish this sentence: *This is my_____*.

🌐 **1.22.B.1.ii** Use letter-sound patterns to spell consonant-vowel-consonant-silent *e* (CVC*e*) words. **1.22.C.1** Spell high-frequency words from a commonly used list.

Name _____

Special Titles

Tell about people who work in your community.
Use words from the box or your own words.
Use titles and names.

teacher   mail carrier   police officer
doctor   vet   librarian

_____
- -
_____

_____
- -
_____

_____
- -
_____

_____
- -
_____

Say other sentences about the people you chose.

School + Home **Home Activity** Your child learned how to use special titles in writing. Write these titles and names on paper: *mr jones, ms gold, dr novak.* Have your child explain what is wrong and write the titles and names correctly.

1.20.A.2.iv Understand and use nouns (proper) in the context of reading, writing, and speaking.

Name _____

Words with Long *i*

Write the list words in the puzzle.

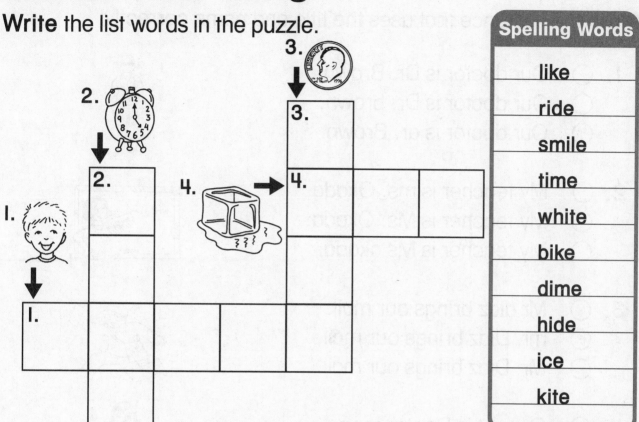

Spelling Words
like
ride
smile
time
white
bike
dime
hide
ice
kite

Draw lines to connect the words that rhyme. Write each word.

5. _____

6. _____

7. _____

8. _____

9. _____

10. _____

School + Home **Home Activity** Your child has been learning to spell words with long *i*. Draw large kite shapes. Have your child write long *i* words on them.

⊕ **1.22.B.1.ii** Use letter-sound patterns to spell consonant-vowel-consonant-silent *e* (CVC*e*) words.

Spelling Words with Long *i*   263

Name _____

Special Titles

Mark the sentence that uses the title and name correctly.

1. ○ Our doctor is Dr. Brown.
   ○ Our doctor is Dr. brown.
   ○ Our doctor is dr. Brown.

2. ○ My teacher is ms. Okada.
   ○ My teacher is Ms. Okada.
   ○ My teacher is Ms okada.

3. ○ Mr diaz brings our mail.
   ○ mr. Diaz brings our mail.
   ○ Mr. Diaz brings our mail.

4. ○ Our vet is Doctor tang.
   ○ Our vet is doctor Tang.
   ○ Our vet is Doctor Tang.

5. ○ miss Vale works at the library.
   ○ Miss Vale works at the library.
   ○ Miss vale works at the library.

6. ○ Mrs. Benik drives our bus.
   ○ Mrs. benik drives our bus.
   ○ mrs. Benik drives our bus.

Home Activity Your child prepared for taking tests on special titles. Together look through a newspaper or magazine. Have your child find and circle as many special titles as he or she can.

✪ 1.20.A.2.iv Understand and use nouns (proper) in the context of reading, writing, and speaking.

Name _____

Write the letters to make a word in each sentence.
Then read the story.

R __ __ **s** __ __ wanted to make soup. She didn't have a

b __ __ **n** __ __ . So she put a big **st** __ __ **n** __ __ in the pot. She

didn't have a **st** __ __ **v** __ __ . She made a fire outside her

h __ __ **m** __ __ . She hung the pot on a **p** __ __ **l** __ __ .

"I **h** __ __ **p** __ __ this will be good," Rose said.

Circle the words that have the same long o sound as .

clove	bond	not	poke	stop	spoke
drop	lost	vote	son	color	told

Home Activity Your child practiced reading words with the long o sound spelled o – e, such as rope. Work with your child to write a list of words that rhyme with bone. Repeat with joke.

1.3.A.1.ii.9 Decode words in context by applying common letter-sound correspondences, including: single letters (vowels) including long o (o_e). **Also 1.3.A.2.ii.9.**

Name _____

Read the words in the box.
Pick a word from the box to match each clue.
Write it on the line.

> **down   inside   now   there   together**

1. not up

_____

---

2. not here

_____

---

3. not outside

_____

---

4. not then

_____

---

5. not one here and not one there

_____

 Home Activity Your child identified and read the words *down, inside, now, there,* and *together.* Read one word aloud. Have your child point to it and use it in a sentence. Repeat with the other words.

⊕ **1.3.H.1** Identify at least 100 high-frequency words from a commonly used list. **Also 1.3.H.2.**

Name _____

Write a number in each box to show the right order.
Then **act out** the story.

1. ☐

2. ☐

3. ☐

Look at each picture.
Draw what will happen next.

4.

5.

Home Activity Your child learned about the order in which things happen in a story. After you read a story with your child, have your child tell you what happened first, next, and last in the story.

RC-1.E.1 Retell important events in stories in logical order.
Also RC-1.E.2, 1.9.A.2.

Name _____

Writing • Poem

 Time for Spines

It is late Monday night.

I go out for a bite.

It is dark out there.

But I am not scared.

Down comes the owl.

I will just bow

And stick out my spines

Because I am a porcupine.

Key Features of a Poem

• It can describe an event.

• The lines may rhyme.

⊕ **1.18.B.1** Write short poems that convey sensory details.

Name _____

Read each sentence.
Write the contraction for the underlined words.

I **do not** think I can do this.   I **don't** think I can do this.

---

1. "I **can not** make a nest," said the little bird.   _____

2. "I **will** need help with the sticks," said
   the little bird.   _____

3. "I **do not** think I can help," said the frog.   _____

4. "**You will** need a big bird to help you,"
   said the frog.   _____

5. "I **am** a big bird! I can help," said
   the big bird.   _____

School + Home   **Home Activity** Your child combined words to form contractions ending with *n't, 'm,* and *'ll*. Say a contraction aloud. Have your child tell you the two words that were combined to make the contraction. Repeat with the other contractions.

1.3.G.1 Identify contractions. **Also 1.3.G.2.**

Phonics Contractions   **269**

Name _____

Words with Long o

Spelling Words				
home	hope	rose	woke	those
bone	hose	joke	rode	stone

Write a list word for each clue.

_____

1. You use it to water the grass. _____

2. You live here. _____

3. It is a part of your body. _____

4. It makes you laugh. _____

5. It grows in a garden. _____

6. It hurts when it gets in your shoe. _____

Write the word that rhymes with each word.

7. smoke

_____

8. rope

_____

9. nose

_____

10. code

_____

those
woke
hope
rode

Home Activity Your child wrote words with long o. Work together to think of other long o words. Take turns making up clues for the new words and guessing them.

1.22.B.1.ii Use letter-sound patterns to spell consonant-vowel-consonant-silent e (CVCe) words.

Name _____

Proper Nouns: Days, Months, Holidays

Days of the week begin with capital letters.

    Sunday   Wednesday   Saturday

Months of the year begin with capital letters.

    February   May   October

Holidays begin with capital letters.

    Fourth of July   Memorial Day

Write the day, month, or holiday correctly on the line.

1. We learn about dinosaurs on monday.

   _____

2. On thursday a man tells us about dinosaurs.

   _____

3. In november we put on a play about dinosaurs.

   _____

4. The play tells about dinosaurs at thanksgiving!

   _____

Home Activity Your child learned about days, months, and holidays. Say the names of a day, a month, and a holiday and help your child write each name. Be sure each name begins with a capital letter.

1.20.A.2.iv Understand and use nouns (proper) in the context of reading, writing, and speaking.

Conventions Proper Nouns **271**

Name _____

Sequence

First

Next

Last

Home Activity Your child is writing a poem about an animal. Have your child describe an animal.

1.18.B.1 Write short poems that convey sensory details.

Name _____

T t

An apostrophe takes the place of missing letters.

Copy the words. Slant all of your letters the same way.

isn't _____

can't _____

Tom _____

don't _____

didn't _____

I'm _____

you'll _____

we'll _____

they'll _____

I'll _____

wasn't _____

won't _____

Did you slant all of your letters the same way? | Yes | | No |

Home Activity Your child practiced writing words with *Tt* and contractions with *'t*. Say the following words and have your child look at the list and write the contraction for them: *can not (can't); they will (they'll); is not (isn't); I am (I'm); can not (can't).*

🌐 1.21.A.1 Form upper-case letters legibly in text, using the basic conventions of print (left-to-right and top-to-bottom progression), including spacing between words and sentences. **Also 1.21.A.2.**

Name _____

Read the newsletter. **Answer** the questions.

The Neighborhood   March

Kids Help!
by Pam Ride

Jill and Sam went for a walk. Mrs. Bell's pet cat was out! The kids could see the cat. They ran to it. They got the cat. Mrs. Bell said, "You are good kids!" She gave them a hug.

---

1. What is the name of the newsletter?

_____

- -

_____

2. What is the name of the story?

_____

- -

_____

3. What is the story about?

_____

- -

_____

_____

- -

_____

Home Activity Your child learned to use a newsletter to get information. As you look at newsletters, newspapers, or magazines, point out the different kinds of type, such as bold or italic text. Discuss why the text looks different from the surrounding type. Then have your child act out a piece of information they learned from researching newsletters, newspapers, or magazines.

1.23.B.1 Decide what sources of information might be relevant to answer these questions. **Also 1.26.A.2.**

What Am I?

Long o: o_e		Contractions n't, 'm, 'll		High-Frequency Words	
nose	rope	I'm	can't	a	what
hole	pole	you'll	isn't	I	me
bone	globe			see	

I'm on a face.

I can't see, but I can smell.

What am I? (I'm a nose!)

I'm a ball that isn't in a game.

You'll see shapes and lines on me.

What am I? (I'm a globe!)

4

Decodable Story *What Am I?*
Target Skill Long *o*: *o_e*, Contractions *n't*, *'m*, *'ll*

🌀 **1.3.A.2.ii.9** Decode words in isolation by applying common letter-sound correspondences, including: single letters (vowels) including long *o* (*o_e*). **Also 1.3.G.2, 1.3.H.2.**

You'll put me in the trash.

A pup puts me in a hole.

What am I? (I'm a bone!)

I'm tall and thin.

You'll see a flag and rope on me.

What am I? (I'm a pole!)

Name _____

Words with Long *o*

Spelling Words				
home	hope	rose	woke	those
bone	hose	joke	rode	stone

High-Frequency Words
there
together

Read about Fluff and Puff. **Write** the missing list words.

Fluff and Puff live by a big **1.** _____ . One day Pup

dug for a **2.** _____ . Pup **3.** _____

Fluff and Puff. He entered their **4.** _____ . Now

5. _____ bunnies needed a new home. They had

little **6.** _____ . Puff **7.** _____ on

Fluff's back as they looked. Then Pup poked up over a

8. _____ bush. Pup pointed over **9.** _____ .

"I found a perfect home. You can live by the bush

_____ "

10. _____ .

Home Activity Your child used spelling words and high-frequency words in a story. Ask your child to write his or her own story, using some of the words.

1.22.B.1.ii Use letter-sound patterns to spell consonant-vowel-consonant-silent *e* (CVC*e*) words. **1.22.C.1** Spell high-frequency words from a commonly used list.

Spelling Words with Long *o* **277**

Proper Nouns: Days, Months, Holidays

Tell about a picnic, a fair, or a party.
Use the name of a month or holiday from the box

February	October	Valentine's Day
May	November	Fourth of July
July	December	Thanksgiving

_____

- -

_____

_____

- -

_____

_____

- -

_____

_____

- -

_____

_____

- -

_____

School + Home

Home Activity Your child learned how to use days, months, and holidays in writing. Write these names on paper: *tuesday, april, memorial day.* Have your child explain what is wrong and write the names correctly.

1.20.A.2.iv Understand and use nouns (proper) in the context of reading, writing, and speaking.

Name _____

Words with Long o

Write the words.

1. _____

2. _____

3. _____

4. _____

Spelling Words

home

hope

rose

woke

those

bone

hose

joke

rode

stone

Write the missing letters. **Write** the list word.

5. **h** __ __ **p** __

_____

6. **th** __ __ __

_____

7. __ __ **d** __

_____

8. **j** __ __ __

_____

9. **h** __ **s** __

_____

10. **w** __ __ **k** __

_____

hope
woke
those
joke
rode
hose

School + Home

Home Activity Your child has been learning to spell words with long o. Have your child think of and write words that rhyme with *nose* or *cone*.

🟊 **1.22.B.1.ii** Use letter-sound patterns to spell consonant-vowel-consonant-silent *e* (CVC*e*) words.

Name _____

Proper Nouns: Days, Months, Holidays

Mark the sentence that uses the day, month, or holiday correctly.

1. ○ On Tuesday we collect cans.
   ○ On tuesday we collect cans.
   ○ On TuesDay we collect cans.

2. ○ A truck picks up the cans on friday.
   ○ A truck picks up the cans on Friday.
   ○ A truck picks up the cans on FRiday.

3. ○ The neighbors plant a garden in june.
   ○ The neighbors plant a garden in JUne.
   ○ The neighbors plant a garden in June.

4. ○ In august they pick the vegetables.
   ○ In August they pick the vegetables.
   ○ In AuGust they pick the vegetables.

5. ○ On memorial Day our town has a parade.
   ○ On Memorial day our town has a parade.
   ○ On Memorial Day our town has a parade.

6. ○ We watch fireworks on the Fourth of July.
   ○ We watch fireworks on the fourth of July.
   ○ We watch fireworks on the Fourth of july.

Home Activity Your child prepared for taking tests on days, months, and holidays. Together look through a newspaper or magazine. Have your child find and circle any days, months, and holidays that he or she finds.

280 Conventions Proper Nouns

1.20.A.2.iv Understand and use nouns (proper) in the context of reading, writing, and speaking.

Name _____

Circle the word for each picture.

 cube

1.

mule   mile

2.

tub   tube

3.

cub   cube

4.

Pete   pet

5.

tug   tune

6.

flat   flute

7.

tub   tube

8.

hug   huge

Find the word that has the same **long u** sound as .
Mark the ⬭ to show your answer.

9. ⬭ rut
⬭ rid
⬭ rule

10. ⬭ cut
⬭ cute
⬭ cup

1.3.B.1 Combine sounds from letters to creat recognizable words.
Also 1.3.A.2.ii.10, 1.3.B.2.

Phonics Long *u: u-e*, Long *e: e-e*   **281**

Name _____

Look at each picture.
Read the words.
Write the word on the line that best fits the picture.

1. find
   around
   _____

2. water
   food
   _____

3. around
   under
   _____

4. grow
   find
   _____

5. water
   under
   _____

6. food
   water
   _____

  School + Home **Home Activity** Your child identified and read the words *around*, *find*, *food*, *grow*, *under*, and *water*. Make up clues for the words on this page. Ask your child to identify the words. Challenge your child to think of some clues too.

1.3.H.1 Identify at least 100 high-frequency words from a commonly used list. **Also 1.3.H.2.**

Name _____

Look at this book cover.
Circle or **write** your answers.

Hal and Sal Take a Trip

By Bob Dog

1. Who wrote this book? _____

2. What do you think this book will be about?

   real dogs   silly dogs   a real trip

3. What do you think this book will be like?

   funny   sad   full of facts

4. Why do you think the writer wrote this book?

   to tell facts about dogs   to make you sad   to make you laugh

5. Would you want to read this book? Why or why not?

   _____
   _____
   _____
   _____
   _____

Home Activity Your child learned to tell what a book might be about by figuring out why it was written. As you read various materials with your child, have your child tell you what he or she thinks each is about and why the author wrote it.

1.13.A.2 Explain the author's purpose in writing about the text.
Also 1.13.A.1

Comprehension Author's Purpose   **283**

Name _____

Writing · Description

 Oh Deer!

Deer live in woods and fields. They eat all kinds of plants.
Deer love apples. They eat apples that fall on the ground. In
the winter they eat leaves. They nibble on branches. They use
their paws to dig snow. Then they eat the nuts and plants they
find. I like watching deer. They are beautiful.

Key Features of a Description

· It tells about real people or things.

· It uses descriptive words.

1.19.A.1 Write brief compositions about topics of interest to
the student.

Name _____

Pick a word from the box to finish each sentence.
Add -ed to each word. **Write** it on the line.

> call   walk   sniff   jump   rest

_____

1. They _____ rope together.

_____

2. Pam _____ June.

_____

3. They _____ to the park.

_____

4. They _____ in the shade.

_____

5. They _____ the flowers.

School + Home

Home Activity Your child practiced writing words ending in -ed, such as *patched*. Ask your child to read each word and use it in a sentence.

1.3.E.1 Read base words with inflectional endings.

Phonics Inflected Ending -ed   **285**

Name _____

Words with Long *u*

Spelling Words				
huge	June	rule	tube	use
cube	cute	flute	rude	mule

Write the list word that names the picture.
Write a list word that rhymes.

1. _____

2. _____

3. _____

4. _____

5. _____

6. _____

Read the meaning. **Write** the list word.

7. very big

8. not polite

9. a month

10. to work with something

_____

| June |
| use |
| rude |
| huge |

School + Home **Home Activity** Your child spelled words with the long *u* vowel sound. Ask your child to name the two letters that occur in every word. (*u* and *e*)

🌐 **1.22.B.1.ii** Use letter-sound patterns to spell consonant-vowel-consonant-silent *e* (CVC*e*) words.

Singular and Plural Nouns

Many nouns add **-s** to mean more than one.

tree

tre**es**

Draw a line from the noun to the correct picture.
Say a sentence for each plural noun.

1.	2.
bug bugs	rocks rock
3.	4.
plants plant	log logs

1.20.A.2.i Understand and use nouns (singular) in the context of
reading, writing, and speaking. **Also 1.20.A.2.ii.**

Name _____

Idea Web

 Home Activity Your child is learning how to describe animals in writing. Ask your child to describe things that one kind of animal does.

⭐ **1.17.A** Plan a first draft by generating ideas for writing.

Name _____

D _____   d _____

Copy the words. Write the letters the correct size.

Duke _____   Dan _____

dusted _____   use _____

hushed _____   these _____

Deke _____   rushed _____

theme _____   rocked _____

eve _____   dashed _____

Did you write all of your letters the correct size? | Yes | | No |

School + Home

Home Activity Your child practiced writing words with *Dd*, long *u*, long *e*, and words that end in *-ed*. Help your child find, read, and copy words from a favorite book.

⊛ **1.21.A.1** Form upper-case letters legibly in text, using the basic conventions of print (left-to-right and top-to-bottom progression), including spacing between words and sentences. **Also 1.21.A.2.**

Name _____

Read each index. **Answer** the questions.

My Book of Animals **Index**	
ants	3
fox	7
lion	10
zebra	27

My Book of Plants **Index**	
blossom	4
flower	12
trees	18
vines	21

1. What can you read about on page 10? _____

2. What page can you find out about vines? _____

Look at the words. **Place** them in the ABC order.

3. Where does **penguin** go?

fox _____ lion   lion _____ zebra

4. Where does **cactus** go?

blossom _____ flower   flower _____ tree

5. Where does **bird** go?

lion _____ zebra   ant _____ fox

Home Activity Your child learned how to use alphabetical order to find information in an index. Ask your child to help you prepare a food-shopping list. Have your child alphabetize the list.

⊕ **1.24.B.1** Use text features in age-appropriate reference works to locate information.

Duke the Mule

Long u / Long e		Inflected Ending -ed		High-Frequency Words	
Pete	mule	yelled	jumped	a	he
cute	cube	handed	helped	is	was
Duke				the	now

Pete has a cute pet.

His pet is Duke the mule.

In June the gate broke.

Duke handed Pete a wire.

Duke helped fix the gate!

Decodable Story *Duke the Mule*
Target Skill Long *u*, Long *e*; Inflected Ending -*ed*

1.3.A.1.ii.7 Decode words in context by applying common letter-sound correspondences, including: single letters (vowels) including long *e* (*e*). **Also** 1.3.A.1.ii.10, 1.3.A.1.ii.6, 1.3.E.1, 1.3.H.2.

Duke had a trick when he was small.

Pete yelled "Jump!"

Then Duke jumped past the cube.

Now Duke is big.

He walks places. He takes naps.

But Duke still has tricks.

Name _____

Words with Long *u*

Pick the word that finishes each sentence.
Write it on the line.

1. Put an ice _____ in the glass.

2. I got to pet the _____ .

3. You can _____ my pen.

4. School is out in _____ .

5. What a _____ kitten!

6. Is there a _____ about that?

7. This apple is _____ !

8. Let's roll the ball down the _____ .

9. Fill the glass with _____ .

10. The bug is _____ the rock.

Spelling Words
huge
June
rule
tube
use
cube
cute
flute
rude
mule

High-Frequency Words
water
under

Home Activity Your child completed sentences by spelling words with long *u*. Write ___*u*___e and have your child fill in the blanks to spell a word.

 1.22.B.1.ii Use letter-sound patterns to spell consonant-vowel-consonant-silent *e* (CVC*e*) words. **1.22.C.1** Spell high-frequency words from a commonly used list.

Spelling Words with Long *u*   **293**

Name _____

Singular and Plural Nouns

Pretend you are in this park.
Tell about the plants and animals you see.

| trees | flowers | squirrels | birds | rabbits |

_____

- -

_____

_____

- -

_____

_____

- -

_____

_____

- -

_____

School + Home

Home Activity Your child learned how to use plural nouns in writing. Read a story together. Ask your child to point out any words he or she sees that mean more than one.

294 **Conventions** Singular and Plural Nouns

⊕ **1.20.A.2.i** Understand and use nouns (singular) in the context of reading, writing, and speaking. **Also 1.20.A.2.ii.**

Name _____

Words with Long *u*

Spelling Words

huge	June	rule	tube	use
cube	cute	flute	rude	mule

Read the clue. **Write** the list word in the puzzle.

Across

3. after May

5. a pipe

6. animal

Down

1. a law

2. pretty

4. square box

Circle the word that is spelled correctly.

7. flute   flut

8. rude   rood

9. huje   huge

10. use   yuse

Home Activity Your child has been learning to spell words with long *u*. Take turns with your child naming and spelling the words.

1.22.B.1.ii Use letter-sound patterns to spell consonant-vowel-consonant-silent *e* (CVC*e*) words.

Name _____

Singular and Plural Nouns

Mark the word that shows more than one.

1. Look at the two frogs.
   - ○ the
   - ○ Look
   - ○ frogs

2. The bird eats the bugs.
   - ○ bugs
   - ○ eat
   - ○ bird

3. The tree has three holes.
   - ○ has
   - ○ holes
   - ○ tree

4. A bear is by the rocks.
   - ○ bear
   - ○ rocks
   - ○ by

5. The squirrel hides the nuts.
   - ○ nuts
   - ○ squirrel
   - ○ The

Home Activity Your child prepared for taking tests on plural nouns. Together look through a newspaper or magazine. Have your child find and circle as many plural nouns as he or she can.

1.20.A.2.ii Understand and use nouns (plural) in the context of reading, writing, and speaking. **Also 1.20.A.2.i.**

Name _____

Help the bee get home.
Read each word.
Draw a line that goes past only the **long e** words.
Write the **long e** words on the lines.

b**ee**

1. _____

2. _____

3. _____

4. _____

5. _____

6. _____

7. _____

8. _____

School + Home

Home Activity Your child practiced reading and writing words with the long e sound spelled e and ee, as in *he* and *jeep*. Have your child make a list of words that rhyme with *seed*. Repeat with *jeep*.

1.3.A.2.ii.7 Decode words in isolation by applying common letter-sound correspondences, including: single letter (vowels) including long e (e). **Also 1.3.A.2.v.5, 1.3.A.1.ii.7, 1.3.A.i.v.5.**

Name _____

Read the words in the box.
Pick a word from the box to match each clue.
Write the words in the puzzles.

also family new other some their

1. not a lot

2. too

3.

4. not old

5. It's not this one. It's the
_____ one.

6. It's not my food.
It's _____ food.

1.3.H.1 Identify at least 100 high-frequency words from a commonly used list. **Also 1.3.H.2.**

Name _____

Look at both pictures.

Write sentences to tell how the pictures are the same and different.

Same

_____

1. _____

_____

_____

2. _____

_____

Dee

Different

_____

3. _____

_____

_____

4. _____

_____

_____

Lee   5. _____

_____

_____

Home Activity Your child used pictures to tell how two things are alike and different. Point out two objects or two pictures to your child. Encourage your child to tell you how they are the same and how they are different.

RC-1.D.1 Make inferences about text. **Also RC-1.D.2.**   **Comprehension** Compare and Contrast   **299**

Name _____

Writing Prompt: Write a paragraph about how you help your community.

    I like to help in my community. I help at the park. On Saturday, I help grown-ups pick up. I help plant flowers in the spring. A bunch of us dress up the park for July 4th. Helping is fun!

1.19.A.1 Write brief compositions about topics of interest to the student.

Name _____

Circle the word for each picture.

 kitten

1.

ramp   rabbit

2.

button   brake

3.

dinner   dent

4.

base   basket

5.

helmet   hello

6.

napkin   name

7.

mask   muffin

8.

wall   walnut

Draw a picture for each word.

9. mitten

10. picnic

Home Activity Your child read words with two syllables that have two consonants in the middle, as in *kitten*. Have your child choose five words from the page and use each word in a sentence.

⊛ 1.3.C.1.i Use common syllabication patterns to decode words, including: closed syllable (CVC).

Phonics Syllables VC/CV   **301**

Name _____

Words with Long *e*

Spelling Words				
be	feet	he	see	we
green	me	she	tree	week

Write the list word that names the picture.

1. _____

2. _____

Write *e* or *ee* to finish the word. **Write** the word.

3. **sh**_____   _____

4. **h**_____   _____

5. **gr**_____**n**   _____

6. **m**_____   _____

7. **s**_____   _____

8. **w**_____**k**   _____

9. **w**_____   _____

10. **b**_____   _____

School + Home

Home Activity Your child spelled words with the long *e* vowel sound. Ask your child to identify two different ways the sound is spelled in the list words. (*e* and *ee*)

1.22.A.1 Use phonological knowledge to match sounds to letters to construct words.

Name _____

Nouns in Sentences

A **noun** names a person, a place, an animal, or a thing. A noun can be in more than one place in a sentence.

Bees live in a **hive.**

Circle the noun in each sentence.
Draw and **color** a picture for each noun.
Say a sentence about your picture.

1. The sun is warm.

2. Look at the bee.

3. Where is the flower?

Home Activity Your child learned about nouns in sentences. Read a story together. Point to a sentence and have your child point to the nouns in the sentence. Continue with other sentences.

1.20.A.2.i Understand and use nouns (singular) in the context of reading, writing, and speaking.

Conventions Nouns in Sentences   **303**

Name _____

Expository Paragraph
Top-Score Response

Focus/Ideas	A good expository paragraph tells important ideas about the main topic.
Organization	A good expository paragraph tells the ideas in an order that makes sense.
Voice	A good expository paragraph shows that you are interested in your topic.
Word Choice	A good expository paragraph uses words that describe.
Sentences	A good expository paragraph has sentences that are different lengths.
Conventions	A good expository paragraph has a noun in every sentence.

Home Activity Your child is learning to write a paragraph about a topic such as insects. Ask your child to tell what kinds of insects live together in groups.

🌐 **1.17** Use elements of the writing process to compose text.

Name _____

B ------ b

Copy the words. Leave the correct space between the letters.

Bee _____   be _____

seed _____   see _____

beet _____   being _____

he _____   cheek _____

she _____   wheel _____

weep _____   seem _____

deep _____   beef _____

Did you leave the correct space between your letters? **Yes** **No**

Home Activity Your child practiced writing words with *Bb* and the long *e* sound as in *bee*. Have your child choose the long *e* words that begin with *b* and write them again.

 1.21.A.1 Form upper-case letters legibly in text, using the basic conventions of print (left-to-right and top-to-bottom progression), including spacing between words and sentences. **Also 1.21.A.2.**

Name _____

Answer the questions.

1. You are reading about bees this week. **Write** three other insects you would like to know more about.

_____   _____   _____

-------------------------   -------------------------   -------------------------

_____   _____   _____

2. **Circle** the insect you want to know more about.
   Write two questions.

_____

_____

_____

3. **Circle** where you would find more information.

   globe   **encyclopedia**   **computer**

Home Activity Your child learned how to identify a topic and ask questions about the topic. Have a discussion with your child about which insects he or she would like to learn about. If possible, visit your local library to find books or other sources of reference about the topic.

1.23.A.1 Generate a list of topics of class-wide interest.
Also 1.23.A.2, 1.23.B.1.

Seeds

Long e: e, ee		VC/CV words	High-Frequency Words
he	needed	happen	to
be	weeds	problems	the
Lee	keep	insects	for
beet	weeks	basket	what
beets	see		watered
seeds	we'll		

Lee had seeds.

He needed to plant the seeds.

"What will the seeds be?" he asked.

Lee picked beets in six weeks.

"See the basket?" asked Lee.

"We'll get beets for lunch!"

Decodable Story *Seeds*
Target Skills Long e, VC/CV Words

1.3.A.1.ii.7 Decode words in context by applying common letter-sound correspondences, including: single letters (vowels) including long e (e). **Also 1.3.A.1.v.5.**

Lee had problems.

Weeds came in.

Lee had to keep insects off.

Lee dug holes for the seeds.

He watered the seeds.

"What will happen?" he asked.

Name _____

Words with Long e

Spelling Words
be   feet   he   see   we
green   me   she   tree   week

High-Frequency Words
some
family

Read the story. **Write** the missing list words.

1. Dad helped _____ build a house for the birds.

2. A bird came the next _____ .

3. Soon _____ laid some eggs.

4. Dad held me up to _____ them.

5. There were three _____ eggs.

6. I asked if _____ could take one inside.

7. Dad said that would not _____ wise.

8. I knew _____ was right.

9. Soon there will be _____ birds.

10. Now a bird _____ lives in the tree.

Home Activity Your child used spelling words to complete a story. Ask your child to use some of the list words in a story about an event in his or her life.

1.22.A.1 Use phonological knowledge to match sounds to letters to construct words. 1.22.C.1 Spell high-frequency words from a commonly used list.

Name _____

Nouns in Sentences

Bees are like a family.
Bees have special jobs.
Do people in your family have special jobs?
Write about the jobs.

_____
- -

_____
- -

_____
- -

_____
- -

_____
- -

_____
- -

Home Activity Your child learned how to use nouns when writing sentences. Take turns with your child telling about jobs that you do at home. Have your child identify any nouns either of you uses in your sentences.

✪ **1.20.A.2.i** Understand and use nouns (singular) in the context of reading, writing, and speaking.

Name _____

Words with Long *e*

Spelling Words				
be	feet	he	see	we
green	me	she	tree	week

Read the clue. **Write** the list word in the puzzle.

Down

1. seven days
2. large plant

Across

3. the color of grass
4. what you stand on

Circle the word that is spelled correctly. **Write** it.

5. b   be   _____

6. we   whe   _____

7. he   hee   _____

8. mee   me   _____

9. se   see   _____

10. she   shee   _____

Home Activity Your child has been learning to spell words with long e. Draw a tree and have your child write words with long e in the branches.

1.22.A.1 Use phonological knowledge to match sounds to letters to construct words.

Spelling Words with Long *e*   **311**

Name _____

Nouns in Sentences

Mark the sentence that has a line under the noun.

1. ○ The bees <u>wake</u> up.
   ○ The <u>bees</u> wake up.
   ○ The bees wake <u>up</u>.

2. ○ Look <u>at</u> the hive.
   ○ Look at <u>the</u> hive.
   ○ Look at the <u>hive</u>.

3. ○ Jan likes sweet <u>honey</u>.
   ○ Jan likes <u>sweet</u> honey.
   ○ Jan <u>likes</u> sweet honey.

4. ○ The workers <u>get</u> mad.
   ○ The workers get <u>mad</u>.
   ○ The <u>workers</u> get mad.

5. ○ Where does <u>pollen</u> come from?
   ○ Where <u>does</u> pollen come from?
   ○ Where does pollen <u>come</u> from?

6. ○ A family <u>lives</u> together.
   ○ A <u>family</u> lives together.
   ○ A family lives <u>together</u>.

Home Activity Your child prepared for taking tests on nouns in sentences. Together read a simple newspaper or magazine article. Have your child circle as many nouns as he or she can find.

1.6.A.4 Identify words that name things (nouns).

Name _____

 fry

 baby

Circle the word for each picture.

1. puppy   put
2. flop   fly
3. muddy   meet
4. bunny   ball

5. crib   cry
6. sit   city
7. sky   skate
8. had   happy

Circle the word to finish each sentence. **Write** it on the line.

_____
- - - - - - - - - - - - - - - - -

9. I didn't eat breakfast and I was very _____.
   hungry   money

_____
- - - - - - - - - - - -

10. After a day at the beach, my bathing suit was not _____.
    dry   my

School + Home

Home Activity Your child practiced reading words with the vowel sounds of *y* heard in *fry* or *baby*. Work with your child to put the above answers into two word lists—one of words in which *y* represents the long *e* sound (*baby*) and one in which it represents the long *i* sound (*fry*).

⭐ 1.3.A.1.ii.11 Decode words in context by applying common letter-sound correspondences, including: single letters (vowels) y= long e. **Also** 1.3.A.1.ii.12, 1.3.A.2.ii.11, 1.3.A.2.ii.12.

Phonics Vowel Sounds of *y*   **313**

Name _____

Read the words in the box. **Pick** a word to finish each sentence.
Write it on the line.

always becomes day everything
nothing stays things

_____

1. Jazzy likes to play all _____ .

_____

2. _____ can stop him!

_____

3. He gets into _____ .

_____

4. He _____ makes a mess.

_____

5. Jazzy _____ in my room.

_____

6. He hides _____ under the bed.

_____

7. He rests when he _____ sleepy.

Home Activity This week your child identified and read the words *always, becomes, day, everything, nothing, stays,* and *things.* Use paper bag puppets to act out a scene using these new words.

1.3.H.1 Identify at least 100 high-frequency words from a commonly used list. **Also 1.3.H.2.**

Name _____

Read the story. **Look** at the pictures.
Write 1, 2, 3 to show the right order.

1. It was a sunny day.

   Tim saw a slide.

   Tim went up the slide.

   Tim came down the slide.

2. **Read** the story.

   Write a sentence that tells what might happen next.

   Then **draw** a picture.

   Polly planted a seed.

   The seed grew into a plant.

   _____

   -

   _____

 Home Activity Your child learned about the order in which events happen in a story. As you read stories with your child, have your child tell you what parts of the story are important and the order in which they happen.

1.9.A.2 Retell a story's beginning, with attention to the sequence of events.

Name _____

Writing • Realistic Story

 The Slide

Beth and Dave liked the park. They liked the big slide. They ran to the park. The big slide was gone!

"Wow!" Beth said. "Look at the new red slide over there!" Dave ran to it.

"It is a tube slide!" They slid down the new slide. They went zig and then zag. They liked it better than the old slide.

Key Features of a Realistic Story

• Characters and events seem real.

• The setting is like a real place.

• The story has a beginning, middle, and end.

🌐 **1.18.A.1** Write brief stories that include a beginning, middle, and end.

Name _____

Circle a word to finish each sentence.
Write it on the line.

 n**o**

He   Hi

_____

- - - - - - - - - - - - - - - -

1. "_____," Luke said.

Hi   He

_____

- - - - - - - - - - - - - - - -

2. _____ is little.

No   Nod

_____

- - - - - - - - - - - - - - - -

3. _____ one can see him.

so   see

_____

- - - - - - - - - - - - - - - -

4. She is _____ big.

bed   be

_____

- - - - - - - - - - - - - - - -

5. He will grow to _____ big too.

 School + Home

Home Activity Your child practiced reading words with the long vowel pattern heard in *me*, *hi*, and *go*. Work with your child to make a list of words with the long *e* sound spelled *e* and the long *o* sound spelled *o*.

🌐 **1.3.C.1.ii** Use common syllabication patterns to decode words, including: open syllable.

Name _____

Words with Vowel Sounds of *y*

Spelling Words
my   by   try   sunny   handy
fly   cry   lucky   silly   puppy

Write five list words that rhyme with **why.**

1. _____

2. _____

3. _____

4. _____

5. _____

Write the missing word.

sunny   silly   lucky   handy   puppy

6. I have a _____ named Spot.

7. Spot likes _____ days.

8. My pup acts _____ .

9. I am _____ at taking care of Spot.

10. I am _____ to have a pup.

Home Activity Your child spelled words in which the long *e* or long *i* sound is spelled *y*. Ask your child to name the letter that is in every list word (*y*) and pronounce its sound (long *e* as in *puppy* or long *i* as in *fly*).

🌐 **1.22.A.1** Use phonological knowledge to match sounds to letters to construct words.

Action Verbs

A **verb** tells what someone or something does.

The girl **jumps**.

The boy **walks**.

Underline the verb in each sentence.
Say a sentence using each verb.

1. The plant grows in the sun.

2. Benny helps Ms. Torres.

3. Mr. Gray works in the neighborhood.

4. Benny wishes for a place to play.

5. Nai Nai plays by the slide.

6. Mom walks down the hall.

1.6.A.1 Identify words that name actions (verbs). **1.20.A.1.ii** Understand and use verbs (present) in the context of reading, writing, and speaking. **1.20.B.1** Speak in complete sentences with correct subject-verb agreement.

Conventions Action Verbs **319**

Name _____

Story Chart

Title _____

Characters

Settings

Beginning

⬇

Middle

⬇

End of Story

Home Activity Your child can plan and then write a brief story. Have him or her tell what happens in the story.

🔹 **1.17.A.1** Plan a first draft by generating ideas for writing.

Name _____

Y

y

Copy the words. Write the letters from left to right.

Yancy _____ sky _____

baby _____ foggy _____

why _____ dusty _____

fly _____ fry _____

silly _____ funny _____

happy _____ hilly _____

shy _____ cry _____

Did you write your letters from left to right? | Yes | | No |

Home Activity Your child practiced writing words with *Yy*. Have your child copy the following sentence as neatly as he or she can. *Why is the street hilly, bumpy, and rocky?*

1.21.A.1 Form upper-case letters legibly in text, using the basic conventions of print (left-to-right and top-to-bottom progression), including spacing between words and sentences. **Also 1.21.A.2.**

Handwriting 321

Name _____

Jan is presenting a report about playgrounds.
Help her gather information.

builder   librarian   children

1. **Circle** who could help Jan find books about playgrounds.

2. **Put a diamond** around who could tell Jan how much it costs to build a playground.

3. **Put a box** around who could help Jan find out which playground toys are the most fun.

4. **Ask** two classmates which playground toy is their favorite. Write their answers.

   _____   _____
   ------------------------   ------------------------
   _____   _____

5. **Share** the information you gathered with your class.

Home Activity Your child learned about interviewing people as sources of information. Talk with your child about the people you rely on when you need information or answers. Ask you child to write two interview questions to ask a member of your family or community.

322 **Research** Gather Information

1.24.A.1 Gather evidence from available sources (natural and personal). **Also 1.24.A.2, 1.26.A.1.**

I'll Try It!

Vowel sounds of y:		Syllable Pattern CV		High-Frequency Words
my	bumpy	hi	hello	said
try	Katy	tiny	Bo	the
Jody	picky	we	no	is
funny	Molly	me		to
mushy	fluffy	be		
yucky	yummy	so		

"Hi!" said Jody.

"Hello!" said the kids.

"We got muffins at the shop."

"Try my muffin," said Molly.

"It is fluffy and yummy."

"No," said Jody. "It is tiny!"

Decodable Story *I'll Try It!*
Target Skills Vowel Sounds of *y*, Syllable Pattern CV

🌐 **1.3.A.2.ii.11** Decode words in isolation by applying common letter-sound correspondences, including: single letters (vowels) including *y* = long *e*. **Also 1.3.A.2.ii.12.**

"My muffin tastes funny.
It is so mushy," said Bo.

"Hand it to me. I'll try it!" Jody yelled.

"My muffin is yucky.
It is bumpy," said Katy.

"Don't be so picky," Jody said.
"I'll try it!"

Words with Vowel Sounds of y

Spelling Words				
my	by	try	sunny	handy
fly	cry	lucky	silly	puppy

High-Frequency Words
things
always

Fill in the circle. **Write** the word.

1. Look at ○ fly ○ my ○ handy bike.   _____

2. Today is a ○ sunny ○ try ○ by day.   _____

3. Did you ○ silly ○ puppy ○ cry?   _____

4. The song is ○ sunny ○ silly ○ my.   _____

5. She was ○ lucky ○ my ○ fly.   _____

6. I ○ try ○ lucky ○ sunny very hard.   _____

7. Bats can ○ silly ○ fly ○ my.   _____

8. Do you have a ○ puppy ○ cry ○ lucky?   _____

9. I see many ○ sunny ○ fly ○ things.   _____

10. We ○ lucky ○ fly ○ always ride the bus.   _____

School + Home

Home Activity Your child wrote spelling words to complete sentences. Read a sentence from this page. Ask your child to spell the list word.

1.22.A.1 Use phonological knowledge to match sounds to letters to construct words. **1.22.C.1** Spell high-frequency words from a commonly used list.

Action Verbs

Write about things you do every day.
Use action verbs from the box or your own words.
Say several sentences and identify the verb.

eat	go	read
sleep	play	talk

_____

- -

_____

_____

- -

_____

_____

- -

_____

_____

- -

_____

_____

- -

_____

Home Activity Your child learned how to use verbs in writing. Take turns with your child telling about things that you do every day. Have your child identify any action verbs either of you uses in your sentences.

1.6.A.1 Identify words that name actions (verbs)
1.20.A.1.ii Understand and use verbs (present) in the context of reading, writing, and speaking.

Name _____

Words with Vowel Sounds of y

Write the letter **y.** Then write the word.

1. fl____ _____

2. pupp____ _____

3. cr____ _____

4. hand____ _____

5. sunn____ _____

6. sill____ _____

7. luck____ _____

Circle the words that rhyme with **fly. Write** the words.

sunny   try   handy   silly   by   my

8. _____   9. _____   10. _____

Home Activity Your child has been learning to spell words in which the long e or long i sound is spelled y. Have your child underline list words with a long i sound and circle list words with a long e sound.

1.22.A.1 Use phonological knowledge to match sounds to letters to construct words.

Action Verbs

Mark the sentence that has a line under the verb.

1. ○ <u>Benny</u> helps Mr. Gray.
   ○ Benny <u>helps</u> Mr. Gray.
   ○ Benny helps <u>Mr.</u> Gray.

2. ○ Mr. Gray lives in the <u>neighborhood</u>.
   ○ Mr. Gray lives in <u>the</u> neighborhood.
   ○ Mr. Gray <u>lives</u> in the neighborhood.

3. ○ We <u>grow</u> plants here.
   ○ We grow plants <u>here</u>.
   ○ We grow <u>plants</u> here.

4. ○ Nai Nai walks to the <u>meeting</u>.
   ○ Nai Nai <u>walks</u> to the meeting.
   ○ <u>Nai Nai</u> walks to the meeting.

5. ○ Benny sees the <u>blue</u> sky.
   ○ Benny sees the blue <u>sky</u>.
   ○ Benny <u>sees</u> the blue sky.

6. ○ <u>Ms. Torres</u> likes this place.
   ○ Ms. Torres <u>likes</u> this place.
   ○ Ms. Torres likes this <u>place</u>.

Home Activity Your child prepared for taking tests on verbs. Together read a short, simple newspaper or magazine article. Have your child circle as many action verbs as he or she can find.

✪ **1.6.A.1** Identify words that name actions (verbs).
1.20.A.1.ii Understand and use verbs (present) in the context of reading, writing, and speaking.

Name _____

 ri**ng**

 ba**nk**

Circle the word for each picture.

1. sink   sing

2. skunk   skate

3. sink   side

4. kink   king

5. wink   wing

6. trunk   truck

7. hand   hang

8. swim   swing

Write the letters **ng** or **nk** to finish the words for each sentence.

9. Please b r i ___ ___ me a d r i ___ ___ .

10. T h a ___ ___ you for the pretty r i ___ ___ .

11. I heard the horn h o ___ ___ .

Home Activity Your child read words that end with *ng* and *nk*. Say one of the words with *ng* or *nk* on this page and ask your child to say a word that rhymes with it. Then have your child say a word for you to rhyme.

1.3.D.1 Decode words with common spelling patterns. **Also** 1.3.A.1.iv.6, 1.3.A.2.iv.6.

Phonics Consonant Patterns *ng*, *nk*   **329**

Name _____

Read the words in the box.
Write a word to finish each sentence.

any	enough	ever
every	own	sure	were

1. Do we have ⬜⬜⬜⬜⬜⬜ food?

2. Yes, I am ⬜⬜⬜⬜ we do.

3. Is ⬜⬜⬜⬜⬜ place set?

4. Yes, they ⬜⬜⬜⬜ set last night.

5. Do you need ⬜⬜⬜ flowers?

6. No, I have my ⬜⬜⬜ .

7. This will be the best day ⬜⬜⬜⬜ !

Home Activity This week your child identified and read the words *any, enough, ever, every, own, sure,* and *were.* Help your child make up a short story using some of these words. Then help your child to write down the sentences and draw a picture to go with his or her story.

⭐ **1.3.H.1** Identify at least 100 high-frequency words from a commonly used list. **Also 1.3.H.2.**

Name _____

Read the stories.
Circle the answer to each question.

Hens

Many hens are white.

But hens can also be red or black.

Some hens can fly a little.

Hens will roll in dust.

A hen can be a pet.

Pigs

Some pigs are pink.

But there are black pigs too.

A pig can be a pet.

Pigs will roll in the mud.

They do this when they are hot.

---

1. Which animal can fly?   hen   pig

2. Which animal rolls in mud?   hen   pig

3. Which animal can be black?   hen and pig   just hen

4. Which animal can be pink?   hen and pig   just pig

5. Which animal can be a pet?   hen and pig   just pig

Home Activity Your child compared and contrasted information in two stories. Have your child choose two birds and tell how the birds are alike and different.

Writing · Comments About a Story

 What I Like About Ruby

I like when Ruby does not eat at first. Sometimes I don't want to eat. I know how she feels. My favorite part is when Ruby flies really high and far. That sounds like fun!

Key Features of Comments About a Story

• comments respond to the story

• tell the writer's opinion or what the writer thinks and feels

1.19.C.1 Write brief comments on literary texts.

Name _____

Pick a word from the box to finish each compound word.
Write it on the line.
Draw a line to the picture it matches.

sidewalk

| ball | cakes | pole | set |

1. pan _____
_____

2. sun _____
_____

3. flag _____
_____

4. base _____
_____

Find the compound word.
Mark the ⬭ to show your answer.

5. ◯ sandy
◯ sandman
◯ sanding

6. ◯ napkin
◯ happen
◯ dishpan

School + Home **Home Activity** Your child read compound words—words formed by joining two or more other words. Walk around your house with your child and find things you see that are compound words *(toothbrush, hairbrush, bathtub)*. Say each word and have your child identify the two words used to make the compound word.

✪ **1.3.F.1** Use knowledge of the meaning of base words to identify common compound words. **Also 1.3.F.2.**

Phonics Compound Words **333**

Name _____

Words with *-ng, -nk*

Look at each picture.
Write two list words that rhyme.

Spelling Words
bring
trunk
pink
bank
sang
wing
rink
blank
rang
sunk

1. _____

2. _____

3. _____

4. _____

5. _____

6. _____

Read the clue. **Write** the word.

7. You keep money in it.   7. _____

8. You did it to a bell.   8. _____

9. You did it to a song.   9. _____

10. You can write a word to fill it.   10. _____

Home Activity Your child spelled words ending in *-ng* and *-nk*. Have your child identify and spell each list word that ends with *-nk*.

1.22.A.1 Use phonological knowledge to match sounds to letters to construct words.

Name _____

Verbs That Add -*s*

A **verb** can tell what one person, animal, or thing does. Add **-s** to show what is being done now.

Ruby **grows** bigger.　　　　Ruby **spreads** her wings.

Complete each sentence.
Write the correct word on the line.
Say a sentence using each verb you wrote.

I. Pam _____ a book.
(reads, read)

2. Ned _____ a cake.
(bake, bakes)

3. José _____ a bike.
(rides, ride)

4. Tina _____ her shoes.
(tie, ties)

School + Home

Home Activity Your child learned about verbs that add -*s*. Write the words *swim, run, walk, jump,* and *dance* on paper. Have your child add an -*s* to each word and then act out the word.

⊛ 1.6.A.1 Identify words that name actions (verbs).
1.20.A.1.ii Understand and use verbs (present) in the context of reading, writing, and speaking.

Conventions Verbs That Add -*s*　　**335**

Name _____

Comments and Feelings

I Like When Ruby . . .	I Feel . . .	Because . . .

Home Activity Your child can express ideas about a story. Ask your child's opinion about the story of Ruby the duck.

1.19.C.1 Write brief comments on literary texts.

Name _____

K ------- K -------

Copy the words. Write the letters from left to right.

King _____ bring _____

long _____ dunk _____

honk _____ thank _____

think _____ Kang _____

tank _____ wing _____

sang _____ clank _____

bank _____ link _____

Did you write your letters from left to right? | **Yes** | | **No** |

Home Activity Your child practiced writing words with *Kk* and words that end in *-nk* or *-ng*. Have your child write words that rhyme with *think*.

1.21.A.1 Form upper-case letters legibly in text, using the basic conventions of print (left-to-right and top-to-bottom progression), including spacing between words and sentences. **Also 1.21.A.2.**

Handwriting 337

Name _____

Find these words in the Glossary of your student book.
Draw a picture to show what each word means.

1. feather

2. mother

3. night

4. rain

5. father

6. flew

Home Activity Your child learned how to use a glossary to look up the meaning of words. Find a glossary in a book at home or at the library and work with your child to look up other words.

1.24.B.1 Use text features in age-appropriate reference works to locate information.

The King Sings a Song

Consonant Patterns *ng* and *nk*		Compound Words		High-Frequency Words	
think	king	upset	anything	a	do
pink	sing	inside	baseball	I	said
thanks	song	himself	hilltop	of	the
honk	long	cannot	rosebuds	to	

A king felt upset.

He sat inside by himself.

"I cannot think of anything to do," he said.

1

"I will sing with them," said the king.

"I will sing a long song.

Then I will be happy!"

4

Decodable Story *The King Sings a Song*
Target Skills Consonant Patterns -*ng* and -*nk*, Compound Words

1.3.A.1.iv.6 Decode words in context by applying common letter-sound correspondences, including: consonant digraphs including *ng*.

"Get the baseball," said the queen.

"We can toss it on the hilltop."

"No, thanks," said the king.

"Take a walk," said the princess.

"See the rosebuds. Pet the pink pigs.

The geese will honk a song."

Name _____

Words with -ng, -nk

Spelling Words				
bring	trunk	pink	bank	sang
wing	rink	blank	rang	sunk

High-Frequency Words
every
sure

Write the missing **ng** or **nk**. **Write** the word.

1. Did you skate at the **ri**_____ ? _____

2. Put the bag in the **tru**_____ . _____

3. The bell **ra**_____ . _____

4. The boat has **su**_____ . _____

5. We clapped as he **sa**_____ . _____

6. I have a piggy **ba**_____ . _____

7. The bird hurt its **wi**_____ . _____

8. Did you paint it **pi**_____ ? _____

Write a high-frequency word to fit each clue.

9. no doubt _____ 10. all _____

School + Home **Home Activity** Your child wrote spelling words to complete sentences. Have your child say and spell the list words with -ng.

1.22.A.1 Use phonological knowledge to match sounds to letters to construct words. 1.22.C.1 Spell high-frequency words from a commonly used list.

Verbs That Add -s

Look at the picture.
Write a verb to finish each sentence.
Remember to add **-s** to each verb.
Add more words to the sentence if you want.

The girl _____.

The boy _____.

The dad _____.

The mom _____.

Choose other verbs. **Say** a sentence for each verb.

1.6.A.1 Identify words that name actions (verbs). **1.20.A.1.ii**
Understand and use verbs (present) in the context of reading, writing, and speaking. **Also 1.22.D.1.**

Name _____

Words with -ng, -nk

Unscramble the letters to make a list word.
Write the word.

1. **k i n p**	1. _____
2. **r n g a**	2. _____
3. **g n i w**	3. _____
4. **n r i k**	4. _____
5. **r t n k u**	5. _____

Spelling Words
bring
trunk
pink
bank
sang
wing
rink
blank
rang
sunk

Write three list words that begin like .

6. _____   7. _____   8. _____

Write two list words that begin like .

9. _____   10. _____

Home Activity Your child has been learning to spell words with -ng or -nk. Have your child spell a list word and use it in a sentence.

1.22.A.1 Use phonological knowledge to match sounds to letters to construct words.

Spelling Words with -ng, -nk   **343**

Verbs That Add -s

Mark the sentence that is correct.

1. ○ Amy plays a song.
    ○ Amys plays a song.
    ○ Amy plays a songs.

2. ○ Johns writes his name.
    ○ John writes his name.
    ○ John writes hiss name.

3. ○ Rosa makes one big pizzas.
    ○ Rosa makes one bigs pizza.
    ○ Rosa makes one big pizza.

4. ○ Daves runs a long race.
    ○ Dave runs a long race.
    ○ Dave runs a longs race.

5. ○ Kate learns a new game.
    ○ Kates learns a new game.
    ○ Kate learns a new games.

6. ○ Sam spells a hards word.
    ○ Sam spells a hard words.
    ○ Sam spells a hard word.

School + Home

Home Activity Your child prepared for taking tests on verbs that add -s. Together read a short, simple newspaper or magazine article. Have your child find and circle as many verbs that end in -s as possible.

✪ **1.6.A.1** Identify words that name actions (verbs). **1.20.A.1.ii** Understand and use verbs (present) in the context of reading, writing, and speaking.

Name _____

Greg fix**es** the bench**es**.

Add the ending.
Write the new word on the line.

Word	Ending	New Word
1. mix	+ -es	_____
2. brush	+ -es	_____
3. glass	+ -es	_____
4. catch	+ -es	_____
5. dress	+ -es	_____
6. bus	+ -es	_____
7. dish	+ -es	_____
8. fox	+ -es	_____
9. nut	+ -s	_____
10. patch	+ -es	_____

School + Home

Home Activity Your child added -es to verbs and nouns. Have your child use each new word in a sentence.

1.3.E.1 Read base words with inflectional changes.

Phonics Endings -es; Plural -es   **345**

Name _____

Read the words in the box.
Pick a word to finish each sentence.
Write it on the line.

> away   car   friends   house   our   school   very

_____
1. This is our new _____ .

_____
2. It is by my _____ .

_____
3. It is _____ nice.

_____
4. We go with our _____ .

_____
5. They come in a _____ .

_____
6. My mom will walk _____ . I will stay.

_____
7. _____ teacher is inside.

Home Activity This week your child identified and read the words *away, car, friends, house, our, school,* and *very*. Use sock puppets to act out a new story using the words. Help your child write down the story you create.

346 **High-Frequency Words**

1.3.H.1 Identified at least 100 high-frequency words from a commonly used list. **Also 1.3.H.2.**

Name _____

Read the story.
Follow the directions.

Kate has a pet bird called Bing.

Her bird is green and red.

A bird is the best pet of all pets.

Bing plays with a bell.

Bing likes to talk.

---

1. **Write** two facts about the story.

_____

- -

_____

- -

_____

- -

_____

- -

_____

2. **Write** the sentence from the story that is an opinion. **Explain**
your answer.

_____

- -

_____

- -

_____

Home Activity Your child has learned about fact and opinion. Discuss the difference between a fact and an opinion. A fact can be proven to be true; an opinion cannot be proven to be true. Have your child tell a fact and an opinion about his or her favorite food.

1.4.B.3 Identify important facts in text, read. **Also RC-1.D.2.**   **Comprehension** Fact and Opinion   **347**

Name _____

Writing Prompt: Write a summary of your favorite story.

Ruby in Her Own Time is my favorite story. Ruby takes longer to do things than her brothers and sisters. She eats later. She swims later. But she flies farthest first. She leaves home. Then she comes back. She brings her new family.

1.19.A.1 Write brief compositions about topics of interest to the student. 1.19.C.1 Write brief comments on literary texts.

Name _____

Circle the word for each picture.

 st<u>or</u>m

 sc<u>ore</u>

1.	2.	3.	4.
fork flick	hen horn	core conk	store stock

5.	6.	7.	8.
con corn	shorts shots	port pot	thorn tone

Find the word that has the same middle sound as .
Mark the ⬭ to show your answer.

9. ⬭ porch
   ⬭ poke
   ⬭ pole

10. ⬭ such
    ⬭ shut
    ⬭ shore

Home Activity Your child read words with *or* as in *storm* and *ore* as in *score*. Help your child make up a story using words with this vowel sound, such as *snore*, *horn*, *popcorn*, and *short*. Then have your child illustrate his or her story.

1.3.C.1.vi.5 Use common syllabication patterns to decode words, including: r-controlled vowel sounds.

Phonics Vowels: *r*-Controlled *or, ore*   **349**

Name _____

Words with -es

Finish the list word. Then **write** the word that means more than one.

_____   _____
1. one **b**_____   2. three _____

_____   _____
3. one **k**_____   4. three _____

_____   _____
5. one **w**_____   6. three _____

Spelling Words
fix
fixes
class
classes
wish
wishes
kiss
kisses
bus
buses

Write the missing word.

_____
7. My _____ has ten boys.

_____
8. Sam _____ clocks.

classes
fix
fixes
class

_____
9. Do the music _____ meet here?

_____
10. Can you _____ my bike?

Home Activity Your child spelled words that end with -es. Say a list word that does not end with -es. Ask your child to add -es and spell the new word.

1.22.D.1 Spell base words with inflectional endings.

Verbs That Do Not Add -s

Do not add **-s** to a verb that tells what two or more people, animals, or things do now.

Meg and Jen **want** a new pet.

Circle the verb that shows more than one.
Say a sentence for each verb you wrote.

1. Meg and Jen (find, finds) some pets.

2. The pets (likes, like) to eat.

3. Pet stores (sell, sells) many pets.

Circle the correct verb. **Write** the verb on the line.

4. The girls _____ many pets.
   (see, sees)

5. The pets _____ to see us.
   (runs, run)

School + Home

Home Activity Your child learned about verbs that do not add -s. Write this sentence beginning: *The children ____.* Then act out a verb, such as *swim, run, walk, jump,* and *dance.* Have your child say the verb to finish the sentence.

Name _____

Writing Rubric
Summary

Top-Score Response

Focus/Ideas	A good summary tells important information.
Organization	A good summary tells the ideas in the correct order.
Voice	A good summary shows that you understand the ideas.
Word Choice	A good summary uses words that describe and show time order.
Sentences	A good summary uses complete sentences.
Conventions	A good summary uses subjects and verbs that go together.

School + Home **Home Activity** Your child is learning how to write a short summary of a story. Read a short story together, and ask you child to briefly retell what happens in the story.

✪ 1.17 Use elements of the writing process to compose text.

Name _____

-------R-------   -------r-------

Copy the words. Write the letters the correct size.

Rory _____   shore _____

for _____   corn _____

store _____   more _____

chore _____   short _____

storm _____   sore _____

born _____   fort _____

torn _____   fork _____

Did you write all of your letters the correct size? | **Yes** | | **No** |

Home Activity Your child practiced writing words with *Rr*, *or*, and *ore*. Have your child read and write any five words from the list one more time.

1.21.A.1 Form upper-case letters legibly in text, using the basic conventions of print (left-to-right and top-to-bottom progression), including spacing between words and sentences. **Also 1.21.A.2.**

Handwriting 353

Name _____

Read Alex's chart with facts he has gathered.
Help him revise his topic.

Facts About	
Mammals	**Reptiles**
have hair on their bodies	have dry skin and no hair
babies born alive	alligators, crocodiles, turtles, snakes
bears, cats, whales, people	

1. Alex's topic is "Facts about Mammals and Reptiles." Does he have the right information to write about that topic? Why or why not?

   ----

2. What additional fact about reptiles might Alex want to find?

   ----

3. Alex wants to revise his topic. Use Alex's chart to choose the topic.

   How mammals and reptiles are alike and different

   How mammals and reptiles live

4. Why is that a better topic for Alex?

Home Activity Your child learned how to review and revise topics. Choose a topic that is of interest to your child. Ask your child to share some facts about this topic with you. Then, using a reference source such as a computer or encyclopedia, read with your child about the topic. Have your child revise his or her list based on the results of your research.

1.25.A.1 Revise the topic (with adult assistance) as a result of answers to initial research questions.

Six Wishes

Ending -*es* and plural -*es*	*r*-controlled *or* and *ore*		High-Frequency Words	
fetches foxes	porch	chores	a	said
hatches buses	for	snored	the	of
wishes boxes	horn	snores	I	is
	more			

Elf sat on the porch.

"I will grant six wishes," said Elf.

"This will be fun," said the foxes.

Funny Fox snored. Elf got a horn.

"I will grant this last wish.

No more snores!" said Elf.

Decodable Story *Six Wishes*
Target Skills Endings -*es*; Plural -*es*; *r*-controlled *or*, *ore*

🅐 1.3.C.1.vi.5 Use common syllabication patterns to decode words, including: *r*-controlled vowel sounds. **Also 1.3.E.1.**

Franny Fox wished for a pet that fetches.

"Can I get a hen that hatches fancy eggs?" asked Freddy Fox.

Sleepy Fox wished for buses.

Winky Fox wished for boxes of dishes.

"My wish is no more chores," said Franky Fox.

Name _____

Words with -es

fix	fixes	class	classes	wish
wishes	kiss	kisses	bus	buses

High-Frequency Words

friends

very

Read about a wish. **Write** the missing list words.

1. I _____ I could visit my aunt.

2. I would go by _____ .

3. I might need to ride on two or three _____ .

4. My aunt _____ hair in her shop.

5. She would _____ my hair.

6. She teaches art _____ , too.

7. I could go to a _____ .

8. I would give my aunt a big _____ .

9. She would give me a _____ big kiss.

10. I hope my _____ meet her.

Home Activity Your child wrote spelling words to complete a story. Ask your child to write about a wish, using some of the list words.

1.22.C.1 Spell high-frequency words from a commonly used list.
1.22.D.1 Spell base words with inflectional endings.

Spelling Words with -es   **357**

Verbs That Do Not Add -s

Pretend you see two new girls at school.
Write about what you do.
Write about what they do.
Begin your sentences with <u>we</u> and <u>they</u>.
Include a sentence that ends with an exclamation point. (!)

_____

_____

_____

_____

_____

_____

Home Activity Your child learned how to use verbs that do not add -s in writing. Point to pictures that show more than one person, animal, or thing. Ask: *What do the (children, birds, etc.) do?* Have your child write the answer to the question.

1.6.A.1 Identify words that name actions (verbs).
1.20.A.1.ii Understand and use verbs (present) in the
context of reading, writing, and speaking. **Also 1.21.C.5.**

Words with -es

Read the clues. **Write** the list words.

Spelling Words
fix
fixes
class
classes
wish
wishes
kiss
kisses
bus
buses

1. It rhymes with **Gus**.
   _____
   - - - - - - - - - - - - - - - - - -
   _____

2. It rhymes with **glass**.
   _____
   - - - - - - - - - - - - - - - - - -
   _____

3. It rhymes with **fishes**.
   _____
   - - - - - - - - - - - - - - - - - -
   _____

4. It rhymes with **dish**.
   _____
   - - - - - - - - - - - - - - - - - -
   _____

5. It rhymes with **mix**.
   _____
   - - - - - - - - - - - - - - - - - -
   _____

6. It rhymes with **miss**.
   _____
   - - - - - - - - - - - - - - - - - -
   _____

Add -es. **Write** the new word in the puzzle.

Down
7. bus
8. fix

Across
9. kiss
10. class

Home Activity Your child has been learning to add -es to words. Have your child write a list word that ends with -es. Then have your child cross out -es to make a different list word.

1.22.D.1 Spell base words with inflectional endings.

Verbs That Do Not Add -s

Mark the sentence that is correct.

1. ○ Ann and Pat walks to a pet store.
    ○ Ann walk to a pet store.
    ○ Ann and Pat walk to a pet store.

2. ○ The girls like their new pets.
    ○ The girls likes their new pets.
    ○ The girl like their new pets.

3. ○ Their pet live in a box.
    ○ Their pets live in a box.
    ○ Their pets lives in a box.

4. ○ Ben and Vic talk to the girls.
    ○ Ben talk to the girls.
    ○ Ben and Vic talks to the girls.

5. ○ The boy tell about the new pet.
    ○ The boys tell about the new pet.
    ○ The boys tells about the new pet.

6. ○ Pat like the mice.
    ○ Ann and Pat likes the mice.
    ○ Ann and Pat like the mice.

Choose other verbs. **Say** a sentence with each verb.

Home Activity Your child prepared for taking tests on verbs that do not add -s. Together read a paragraph from a newspaper or magazine article. Have your child find and circle verbs that do not end in -s.

 1.6.A.1 Identify words that name actions (verbs).
1.20.A.1.ii Understand and use verbs (present) in the context of reading, writing, and speaking.

Name _____

Dan is mop**ping** up the mess.
The mess is mop**ped** up.

Add -ed and **-ing** to each word.
Write the new words on the lines.

Add -ed	Add -ing
1. nap		
2. pat		
3. nod		
4. jog		
5. wag		
6. stop		
7. pet		
8. drop		
9. clap		
10. plan		

Home Activity Your child practiced writing words that end in -ed and -ing. Together with your child make up a story using the words above.

1.3.E.1 Read base words with inflectional endings.

Name _____

Circle a word to finish each sentence.
Write it on the line.

how   few

_____

1. We have a _____ 📖 to take back.

---

afraid   read

_____

2. We _____ them all and came for new ones.

again   few

_____

3. Can we get some _____ ?

---

soon   how

_____

4. We can read _____ to plant flowers.

---

afraid   few

_____

5. I am _____ this is not the best one.

---

afraid   soon

_____

6. My mom will be here _____ .

Home Activity This week your child identified and read the words *afraid, again, few, how, read,* and *soon.*
Make some flash cards and have your child practice reading the words.

1.3.H.1 Identify at least 100 high-frequency words from a commonly used list. **Also 1.3.H.2.**

Name _____

Read the story.

Circle or write the answer to each question.

Skunks are always black and white.

Some skunks are black with white spots.

Skunks eat at sunset.

Skunks are good at digging.

They dig to find bugs to eat.

1. What is this story about?

   bugs   skunks   sunsets

2. Why do you think the writer wrote this story? Explain your answer.

   to make you laugh   to make you sad   to tell facts

   _____

   _____

3. What are two things the story tells about skunks?

   _____

   _____

   _____

   _____

   _____

Home Activity Your child read an informational story and figured out why it was written. Read a funny story with your child and talk about why the author wrote it.

1.13.A.2 Explain the author's purpose in writing about the text.
Also RC-1.D.1, RC-1.D.2.

Name _____

Writing • Lists

Things That Helped

Toad planted the seeds in the ground.

Toad let the seeds get rain.

Things That Did Not Help

Toad told the seeds to grow.

Toad read a story to the seeds.

Key Features of a List

• has words or sentences written one below the other

• can have a heading

1.19.C Write brief comments on literary or informational texts.

Name _____

Circle the word for each picture.

 f<u>a</u>rm

1.	2.	3.	4.
arm am	band barn	core car	far jam

5.	6.	7.	8.
duck dark	party patty	cart cork	cord card

Find the word that rhymes with ☆.
Mark the ⊂⊃ to show your answer.

9. ⊂⊃ form
   ⊂⊃ far
   ⊂⊃ for

10. ⊂⊃ tar
    ⊂⊃ torn
    ⊂⊃ trap

 School + Home

Home Activity Your child read words with *ar* as in *farm*. Help your child make up a story about a car trip. Encourage your child to use words with *ar* that have the same vowel sound as *car*.

🌐 **1.3.C.1.vi.4** Use common syllabication patterns to decode words, including: r-controlled vowel sounds.

Phonics Vowel: *r*-Controlled *ar*   **365**

Name _____

Words with -ed

Write the list word to finish the chart.

Base Word	-ed Word
1. _____	**asked**
2. **drop**	_____
3. _____	**helped**
4. **plan**	_____

Spelling Words

ask

asked

plan

planned

help

helped

drop

dropped

call

called

Read the clues. **Write** the list word.

It rhymes with

It starts with **pl.**

It rhymes with

It starts with **c.**

It rhymes with

It starts with **dr.**

5. _____

6. _____

7. _____

Write the list word that tells what happened in the past.

8. We can <u>ask</u> for paper. We _____ for paper.

9. I will <u>call</u> my friends. I _____ my friends.

10. He can <u>help</u>. He _____ .

 Home Activity Your child spelled words that do and do not end with *-ed*. Say a list word that does not end with *-ed*. Have your child say and spell the corresponding *-ed* word.

🌐 **1.22.B.1.iii** Use letter-sound patterns to spell one-syllable words with consonant blends. **1.22.D.1** Spell base words with inflectional endings.

Name _____

Verbs for Past and for Future

A verb can tell what happened in the past. Some verbs that tell about the past end with **-ed.** A verb can tell what happens in the future. It can begin with **will.**

Frog **walked.** (past)   Frog **will walk.** (future)

Read each word in the box. **Write** the word under *The Past* if it tells about the past. **Write** the word under *The Future* if it tells about the future. **Say** each verb you wrote in a sentence.

> will tell   liked   jumped
> helped   will play   will ask

The Past

1. _____

2. _____

3. _____

The Future

4. _____

5. _____

6. _____

School + Home

Home Activity Your child learned about verbs for the past and for the future. Write the words *talk, laugh,* and *yell* on paper. Have your child add *-ed* or *will* to make a verb for the past and a verb for the future.

Name _____

Idea Web

Home Activity Your child can write about the actions of characters in stories. Share a memory about a story you have heard or read with your child and why characters did things.

1.17.A.1 Plan a first draft by generating ideas for writing.

Name _____

-----C----------------------------   -------C--------------

Copy the words. Leave the correct space between your letters.

Carl   _____   Cal   _____

car   _____   cape   _____

barn   _____   harm   _____

start   _____   jar   _____

chart   _____   star   _____

part   _____   bark   _____

card   _____   dark   _____

Did you leave the correct space between your letters? | **Yes** | | **No** |

Home Activity Your child practiced writing words with *Cc* and *ar*. Have your child find three words from the list that rhyme with *far* and write them one more time. (*car, jar, star*)

⊕ 1.21.A.1 Form upper-case letters legibly in text, using the basic conventions of print (left-to-right and top-to-bottom progression), including spacing between words and sentences. **Also 1.21.A.2.**

Handwriting 369

Name _____

We use our eyes to gather information.
Look at the storm. **Write** what you see.

1. Where does the rain come from? _____

2. How many bolts of lightning do you see? _____

3. Do you see a cloud? Circle a cloud.

4. Think about what you know about
storms. What part makes you wet? _____

5. Ask a local expert, such as a weather reporter, questions about
storms. Write the answer.
_____
_____

Home Activity Your child made observations from a natural source and recorded those observations. As you interact with your child this week, point out what can be observed in our homes and in nature.

1.24.A.1 Gather evidence from available sources (natural and personal).

The Cart

Adding endings-double final consonants		r-controlled *ar*		High-Frequency Words	
humming	grabbed	Arty	started	a	said
running	stepped	cart	Marny	I	to
quitting	stopped	park	barked	the	is
getting	hugged	yard	bark		
begged					

Dad made Arty a black cart.

"Can I drive at the park?" begged Arty.

"No. Drive in the yard," said Dad.

"I'm not quitting," Arty yelled to Dad.

"Marny is getting in the cart."

This time he had a happy bark!

Decodable Story *The Cart*
Target Skills Adding Endings, *r*-controlled *ar*

1.3.C.1.vi.4 Use common syllabication patterns to decode words, including: *r*-controlled vowel sounds.

Arty began humming.

He grabbed the wheel and stepped on the gas.

The cart started!

Marny the dog began running beside Arty.

He barked a sad bark.

Arty stopped the cart and hugged Marny.

Name _____

Words with -ed

Spelling Words					High-Frequency Words
ask	asked	plan	planned	help	again
helped	drop	dropped	call	called	soon

Write the missing list words.

_____

1. He _____ if I could come.

_____

2. We have not _____ a trip.

_____

3. She _____ a pen.

_____

4. Has your mom _____ you back home?

_____

5. Jack _____ clean.

_____

6. Did you _____ your dog?

_____

7. I will _____ for more.

_____

8. Tom likes to _____ and run.

_____

9. Liz will have a plan _____ .

_____

10. I jogged on the path _____ .

Home Activity Your child wrote words that end with *-ed* and their base words. Ask your child to find two words in which the final consonant was doubled before adding *-ed* (*plan/planned, jog/jogged*).

⭐ 1.22.B.1.iii Use letter-sound patterns to spell one-syllable words with consonant blends. **1.22.D.1** Spell base words with inflectional endings. Also 1.22.C.1.

Spelling Words with *-ed* **373**

Name _____

Verbs for Past and for Future

In the past you were a baby.
Tell about things you did then.

_____
- -
_____
- -
_____
- -
_____

Now you are in first grade.
Tell about things you will do in the future.

_____
- -
_____
- -
_____
- -
_____

Say the verbs you wrote. **Use** each verb in a sentence.

Home Activity Your child learned about verbs for the past and for the future. With your child, look through a family photo album. Talk about what you were doing then using verbs for the past. Talk about what you might be doing in the future.

🌐 **1.20.A.1.** Understand and use verbs (past) in the context of reading, writing, and speaking. **1.20.A.1.iii** Understand and use verbs (future) in the context of reading, writing, and speaking

Name _____

Words with -ed

Read the base word. **Write** the -ed word in the puzzle.

Across
2. drop   4. call
5. help

Down
1. ask
3. plan

Spelling Words

ask

asked

plan

planned

help

helped

drop

dropped

call

called

Circle the word that is spelled correctly.

6. plan   plann   7. asc   ask

8. cal   call   9. help   halp

10. drop   dropp

Home Activity Your child has been learning to add -ed to base words. Have your child write a list word that ends with -ed. Then have your child cross out the ending (-ed or consonant + -ed) to find the base word.

🌐 **1.22.B.1.iii** Use letter-sound patterns to spell one-syllable words with consonant blends. **1.22.D.1** Spell base words with inflectional endings.

Spelling Words with -ed   **375**

Verbs for Past and for Future

Mark the sentence that is correct.

1. ○ Last week Frog planted seeds in the garden.
   ○ Last week Frog plants seeds in the garden.
   ○ Last week Frog plant seeds in the garden.

2. ○ Soon Toad plant seeds.
   ○ Soon Toad will plant seeds.
   ○ Soon Toad planted seeds.

3. ○ Tomorrow the seeds will start to grow.
   ○ Tomorrow the seeds started to grow.
   ○ Tomorrow the seeds start to grow.

4. ○ Yesterday Frog will shout at Toad.
   ○ Yesterday Frog shouted at Toad.
   ○ Yesterday Frog shouts at Toad.

5. ○ Last week the sun shined.
   ○ Last week the sun shine.
   ○ Last week the sun shines.

6. ○ Tomorrow Toad looks at his garden.
   ○ Tomorrow Toad looked at his garden.
   ○ Tomorrow Toad will look at his garden.

Say sentences using verbs for the past and for the future.

School + Home **Home Activity** Your child prepared for taking tests on verbs for the past and for the future. Together read part of a newspaper or magazine article. Have your child find verbs that tell about the past or the future.

✪ **1.20.A.1.** Understand and use verbs (past) in the context of reading, writing, and speaking. **1.20.A.1.iii** Understand and use verbs (future) in the context of reading, writing, and speaking.

Name _____

h**er**   b**ir**d   s**ur**f

Circle the word for each picture.

1.	2.	3.	4.
short shirt	clerk click	curl chill	barn burn

5.	6.	7.	8.
fern fan	skirt skit	fist first	stir store

Find the word that has the same vowel sound as .
Mark the ⬭ to show your answer.

9. ⬭ hard
    ⬭ hut
    ⬭ hurt

10. ⬭ torn
     ⬭ turn
     ⬭ tune

 School + Home   **Home Activity** Your child read words spelled with *er, ir,* and *ur* that have the same vowel sound as *bird*. Help your child make up rhymes using words with this vowel sound spelled *er, ir, ur*. For example, *You can't wear that shirt. It is covered in dirt!*

⭐ **1.3.C.1.iv.1** Use common syllabication patterns to decode words, including: r-controlled vowel sounds. **Also 1.3.C.1.vi.2, 1.3.C.1.vi.3.**

Phonics Vowels: *r*-Controlled *er, ir, ur*   **377**

Name _____

Read the words in the box.
Pick a word to finish each sentence.
Write the words in the puzzles.

push   visit   wait

1. We'll _____ our
   friends soon.

2. They will _____ us
   on the swings.

3. I can not _____ !

---

done   know

4. I _____ we will do well!

5. We will try to win.
   We will be happy
   when we are _____ .

Home Activity Your child identified and read the words *done, know, push, visit,* and *wait.* Write the words on a sheet of paper. Give your child a clue for each word. Then have him or her guess the word and point to it.

1.3.H.1 Identify at least 100 high-frequency words from a commonly used list. **Also 1.3.H.2.**

Name _____

Read the story.
Follow the directions.

Hand drums are fun to play.

You don't use sticks.

You tap on the top of the drum with your hands.

In the past, people made hand drums from trees.

They made the tops of the drums with animal skins.

1. **Write** two facts from the story.

_____
- -
_____
- -
_____
- -
_____
- -
_____
- -
_____

2. **Write** the sentence from the story that is an opinion.

_____
- -
_____
- -
_____

Home Activity Your child has learned about fact and opinion. Review the difference between a fact and an opinion. A fact can be proven to be true; an opinion cannot be proven to be true. Have your child tell a fact and an opinion about one of the seasons of the year.

1.14.B.1 Identify important facts in text, read. **Also RC-1.D.1.**

Comprehension Fact and Opinion **379**

Name _____

Writing • Captions and Pictures

The bird is yellow in summer.

Now the bird is brown. It changed color in winter.

Key Features of Captions and Pictures

· Captions tell about what pictures show.

· Many captions are sentences.

1.19.A.1 Write brief compositions about topics of interest to the student.

Name _____

Pick a word from the box that means the same as each pair of words. **Write** it on the line.

<u>She is</u> tall.
<u>She's</u> tall.

he's	it's	I've	that's	they're
they've	we're	we've	you're	you've

1. I + have
_____
- - - - - - - - - - - - - - -

2. we + are
_____
- - - - - - - - - - - - - - -

3. it + is
_____
- - - - - - - - - - - - - - -

4. that + is
_____
- - - - - - - - - - - - - - -

5. you + have
_____
- - - - - - - - - - - - - - -

6. they + have
_____
- - - - - - - - - - - - - - -

7. we + have
_____
- - - - - - - - - - - - - - -

8. he + is
_____
- - - - - - - - - - - - - - -

9. they + are
_____
- - - - - - - - - - - - - - -

10. you + are
_____
- - - - - - - - - - - - - - -

School + Home

Home Activity Your child practiced making contractions with *'s, 've,* and *'re*. Read each contraction on this page aloud. Challenge your child to use each one in a sentence. Then work together to write each sentence.

🌐 **1.3.G.1** Identify contractions. **Also 1.3.G.2.**

Phonics Contractions **381**

Words with *er, ir, ur*

Spelling Words				
her	first	bird	girl	burn
were	shirt	fur	hurt	sir

Read the clues. **Write** the list word.

It starts like

It rhymes with **bur.**

1. _____

It starts like

It rhymes with **dirt.**

2. _____

It starts like

It rhymes with **turn.**

3. _____

Write the list word that means the opposite.

4. last _____

5. boy _____

6. heal _____

7. him _____

Write the missing list word.

sir	were	bird

8. We saw a _____ .

9. May I help you, _____ ?

10. We _____ at a pond.

Home Activity Your child spelled words with *er, ir,* and *ur*. Have your child circle these letter Combinations in the list words.

1.22.A.1 Use phonological knowledge to match sounds to letters to construct words.

Name _____

Verbs: *Am, Is, Are, Was, Were*

The words **am, is,** and **are** tell about now. Use **am** or **is** to tell about one. Use **are** to tell about more than one.

I **am** big.

It **is** little.

They **are** tiny.

The words **was** and **were** tell about the past. Use **was** to tell about one. Use **were** to tell about more than one.

It **was** hungry.

They **were** hungry.

Circle the verb in each sentence. **Write Now** if the sentence tells about now. **Write Past** if the sentence tells about the past.

1. I was an egg. _____

2. I am a caterpillar. _____

3. They are caterpillars. _____

4. They were eggs. _____

5. The change is amazing. _____

Home Activity Your child learned about *am, is, are, was,* and *were*. Read a story with your child. Have your child point out the verbs *am, is, are, was,* and *were* in the story and tell whether the sentence tells about now or the past.

1.20.A.1.i Understand and use verbs (past) in the context of reading, writing, and speaking. **1.20.A.1.ii** Understand and use verbs (present) in the context of reading, writing, and speaking.

Conventions Verbs: *Am, Is, Are, Was, Were* **383**

Name _____

Picture Plan

Picture I

Caption: _____

Picture 2

Caption: _____

Home Activity Your child is writing captions. Together, look at pictures in children's books and read captions.

1.17.A Plan a first draft by generating ideas for writing.

Name _____

V v

An apostrophe takes the place of missing letters.

→'

've

Copy the words. Write the letters from left to right.

Val _____   Van _____

I've _____   hive _____

vine _____   we've _____

you've _____   vest _____

five _____   Vicky _____

haven't _____ dive _____

could've _____ they've _____

Did you write your letters from left to right? | **Yes** | | **No** |

Home Activity Your child practiced writing words with *Vv* and contractions with *'ve*. Say the words that form some contractions on this page, and have your child write the contractions one more time: *I have (I've); you have (you've); we have (we've); they have (they've); could have (could've).*

1.21.A.1 Form upper-case letters legibly in text, using the basic conventions of print (left-to-right and top-to-bottom progression), including spacing between words and sentences. **Also 1.21.A.2.**

Name _____

We use our eyes to gather information.
Look at the park. **Write** what you see.

_____

1. What is the man doing? _____

2. Do you see things that fly? **Circle** them.

_____

3. How many people do you see in the park? _____

4. **Write** two questions that you would ask the people in the park.

_____

_____

_____

_____

Home Activity Your child made observations from a natural source and recorded those observations. As you interact with your child this week, point out what can be observed in our homes and in nature.

1.24.A.1 Gather evidence from available sources (natural and personal).

Helping Mom

r-controlled *er, ir, ur*	Contractions	High-Frequency Words	
Fern	I've	said	to
her	I'll	the	play
shirts	can't	I	
skirts	we're	you	
dirty	you'll	is	

"I've got sixteen jobs on my list," said Mom.

"I'll need all the help I can get."

Fern and Kurt grinned.

"We're glad to help."

Then you'll get to play a game with us!"

Decodable Story *Helping Mom*
Target Skills *r*-controlled *er, ir, ur;* Contractions

🌐 **1.3.C.1.vi.1** Use common syllabication patterns to decode words, including: *r*-controlled vowel sounds. **Also 1.3.C.1.vi.2, 1.3.C.1.vi.3, 1.3.G.1, 1.3.G.2.**

"Fern, will you hang up these shirts and skirts?" asked Mom.

"Will you brush the dog? Her fur is dirty."

"Kurt, will you feed the bird?" asked Mom.

"Will you stir the gumbo? We can't let it burn."

Name _____

Words with *er, ir, ur*

Circle the word that is spelled correctly. **Write** it.

1. I like your ____.

   shert   **shirt**   shurt

2. I knew where you ____.

   were   wir   wure

3. Meet the new ____.

   gerl   **girl**   gurl

4. Let the candle ____.

   bern   birn   **burn**

5. Judy said, "Yes, ____."

   ser   **sir**   sur

6. Look at the ____.

   berd   **bird**   burd

7. Can I be ____?

   ferst   **first**   furst

8. His dog has black ____.

   fer   fure   **fur**

9. Are you ____?

   dun   dune   **done**

10. Let's ____ our friends.

    visit   visot   visat

_____

- - - - - - - - - - - - - - - - - - -

_____

_____

- - - - - - - - - - - - - - - - - - -

_____

_____

- - - - - - - - - - - - - - - - - - -

_____

_____

- - - - - - - - - - - - - - - - - - -

_____

_____

- - - - - - - - - - - - - - - - - - -

_____

_____

- - - - - - - - - - - - - - - - - - -

_____

_____

- - - - - - - - - - - - - - - - - - -

_____

_____

- - - - - - - - - - - - - - - - - - -

_____

_____

- - - - - - - - - - - - - - - - - - -

_____

Spelling Words

her
first
bird
girl
burn
were
shirt
fur
hurt
sir

High-Frequency Words

visit
done

School + Home

Home Activity Your child used spelling words in sentences. Help your child make up a new sentence for each spelling word.

1.22.A.1 Use phonological knowledge to match sounds to letters to construct words. 1.22.C.1 Spell high-frequency words from a commonly used list.

Verbs: *Am, Is, Are, Was, Were*

Look at the picture.
Tell about what you see.
Use am, is, are, was, or **were.**

_____

_____

_____

_____

_____

_____

_____

Read the question. **Change** the words to write the answer.
Is that a bird?

_____

_____

Home Activity Your child learned how to use *am, is, are, was,* and *were* in writing. Write these sentence frames on paper: *Today I ____ happy. Now he ____ happy. Yesterday she ____ happy. Now they ____ happy. Yesterday we ____ happy.* Have your child complete the sentences with *am, is, are, was,* and *were.*

1.20.A.1.i Understand and use verbs (past) in the context of reading, writing, and speaking. **1.20.A.1.ii** Understand and use verbs (present) in the context of reading, writing, and speaking.

Name _____

Words with *er, ir, ur*

Spelling Words				
her	first	bird	girl	burn
were	shirt	fur	hurt	sir

Use this code. **Write** the words.

1. _____

2. _____

3. _____

4. _____

5. _____

6. _____

Draw a line through the word that does not match.
Then **write** the word that matches.

7. were   where   were   _____

8. bird   bird   bid   _____

9. grill   girl   girl   _____

10. burn   turn   burn   _____

Home Activity Your child has been learning to spell words with *er, ir,* and *ur*. Write a list word, but replace the letter before *r* with a blank (b__rd). Ask your child to correctly fill in the blank.

1.22.A.1 Use phonological knowledge to match sounds to letters
to construct words.

Spelling Words with *er, ir, ur* **391**

Name _____

Verbs: *Am, Is, Are, Was, Were*

Mark the sentence that is correct.

1. ○ The caterpillar is in the tree.
    ○ The caterpillar am in the tree.
    ○ The caterpillar are in the tree.

2. ○ The bees is on the flowers.
    ○ The bees was on the flowers.
    ○ The bees are on the flowers.

3. ○ One bird were yellow.
    ○ One bird was yellow.
    ○ One bird are yellow.

4. ○ Those roses am red.
    ○ Those roses was red.
    ○ Those roses were red.

5. ○ I am next to the butterfly.
    ○ I are next to the butterfly.
    ○ I is next to the butterfly.

6. ○ We am happy in the trees.
    ○ We are happy in the trees.
    ○ We was happy in the trees.

Home Activity Your child prepared for taking tests on *am, is, are, was,* and *were.* Together read part of a newspaper or magazine article. Have your child circle the verbs *am, is, are, was,* and *were.*

✪ **1.20.A.1.i** Understand and use verbs (past) in the context of reading, writing, and speaking. **1.20.A.1.ii** Understand and use verbs (present) in the context of reading, writing, and speaking.

Name _____

Circle the word for each picture.

small   small**er**   small**est**

1.

faster   fastest

2.

bigger   biggest

3.

taller   tallest

4.

sweeter   sweetest

5.

book image

thicker   thickest

6.

thinner   thinnest

Write -er or **-est** to finish the word in each sentence.

7. The little bird has the few _____ eggs.

8. The little bird has a long _____ tail than
the big bird.

Home Activity Your child identified the comparative endings -er and -est as in *smaller* and *smallest*.
Discuss the sizes, shapes, and colors of animals. Have your child compare the animals using -er when
comparing two and -est when comparing more than two.

1.3.E.1 Read base words with inflectional endings.

Phonics Comparative Endings -er, -est   **393**

Name _____

Read the words in the box.
Pick a word that is the opposite of each word below.
Write it on the line.

┌───┐
│   before   good-bye   right   won't   │
└───┘

1. after

_____

- - - - - - - - - - - - - - - - -

2. will

_____

- - - - - - - - - - - - - - - - -

3. hello

_____

- - - - - - - - - - - - - - - - -

4. wrong

$$\begin{array}{r} 2 \\ +2 \\ \hline 4 \end{array}$$

_____

- - - - - - - - - - - - - - - - -

Pick a word from the box to finish each sentence.
Write it on the line. **Remember** to use capital letters.

┌─────────────────┐
│   oh   does   │
└─────────────────┘

_____

- - - - - - - - - - - - -

5. _____ a bear start its long sleep in the spring?

_____

- - - - - - - - - - - - -

6. _____ , no. It sleeps when the days start to get cold.

Home Activity Your child identified and read the words *before*, *good-bye*, *right*, and *won't*. Write the
opposite of these words on cards and mix them up. Have your child match the words that are opposites and
then read the pairs. Then have him or her write two sentences using *does* and *oh*.

1.3.H.1 Identify at least 100 high-frequency words from a
commonly used list. **Also 1.3.H.2.**

Name _____

Read the story.

Circle the answer to each question.

Zak has a puppy with the name Sparky.

Zak is sitting on his bed.

Sparky puts his nose under the bed.

1. Why do you think Sparky puts his nose under the bed?

   Sparky wants to get up on the bed.

   Sparky wants something under the bed.

Zak finds a ball under the bed.

Sparky starts barking!

2. Why do you think Sparky starts barking?

   Sparky wants to play with the ball.

   Sparky wants Zak to pet him.

Then Zak starts to go outside.

Sparky jumps up and down!

3. Why do you think Sparky jumps up and down?

   Sparky likes to jump up and down.

   Sparky wants to play outside with Zak.

Home Activity Your child drew conclusions about a story. Reread the story with your child. Have your child tell you what he or she already knew about dogs that helped him or her draw conclusions.

🌐 1.9 Draw conclusions about the structure and elements of fiction.

Comprehension Draw Conclusions **395**

Name _____

Writing • Play Scene

 A Friendly Phone Call

Goose: Hello?

Raccoon: Hi, Goose! How are you?

Squirrel: We wish you were here!

Goose: I miss my friends. But I can't stand the cold.

Raccoon: It sure is cold here. We went ice skating.

Goose: I went fishing today.

Squirrel: When will you come home?

Goose: I will be back in spring.

Raccoon: We can't wait!

Squirrel: 'Bye, Goose.

Key Features of a Play Scene

• is written to be acted for an audience

• characters have lines to say

1.18.A.1 Write brief stories that include a beginning, middle, and end.

Name _____

Read each word in the box. **Pick** a word from the box to finish each sentence. **Write** it on the line. **Read** each completed sentence.

fudge	hedge	judge	ledge	smudge

ba**dge**

1. Mom made _____ for us to eat.

2. She set it on the _____ .

3. Did it fall into the _____ ?

4. Look, there's a _____ on Bear's face.

5. The _____ thinks Bear ate it too.

Home Activity Your child learned to read words that end with *-dge* that have the sound heard in *judge*. Have your child make a list of words that rhyme with *judge*.

1.3.A.2.iv.9 Decode words in isolation by applying common letter-sound correspondences, including: consonant digraphs including *-dge*. Also 1.3.A.1.iv.9.

Phonics Consonant Pattern *-dge* 397

Name _____

Words with -er, -est

Spelling Words				
bigger	biggest	faster	fastest	taller
tallest	shorter	shortest	sadder	saddest

Look at the pictures. **Write** list words that end with **-er** and **-est**.

short

1. _____ 2. _____

fast

3. _____ 4. _____

big

5. _____ 6. _____

Write a list word that rhymes with the underlined word.

7. This plant is <u>smaller</u> than that _____ one.

8. The forest has the <u>smallest</u> and the _____ trees.

9. His face grew _____ as he put away the <u>ladder</u>.

10. This is the _____ and the <u>maddest</u> he's ever been.

Home Activity Your child spelled words that end with -er and -est. Say a base word, such as big. Ask your child to say and spell the -er and -est words (bigger, biggest).

1.22.A.1 Use phonological knowledge to match sounds to letters to construct words.

Contractions with *Not*

A **contraction** is a short way to put two words together. A **verb** and the word **not** can be put together to make a contraction. An **apostrophe (')** is used in place of the letter **o** in **not**.

are + not = aren't   has + not = hasn't
did + not = didn't   is + not = isn't
do + not = don't   was + not = wasn't
does + not = doesn't   were + not = weren't

Circle the contraction in each sentence.

1. The animals don't have much time.

2. Caterpillar doesn't come out until spring.

3. Goose isn't staying for the winter.

Write the contraction for the underlined words.

_____
- - - - - - - - - - - - - - - -

4. The leaves <u>are not</u> on the trees.   _____

_____
- - - - - - - - - - - - - - - -

5. Raccoon <u>was not</u> leaving the forest.   _____

Home Activity Your child learned about contractions with *not*. Read a story with your child. Have your child look for contractions with *not* and tell the two words that were put together to make each contraction.

1.3.G.1 Identify contractions. 1.3.G.2 Read contractions.

Name _____

Idea Web

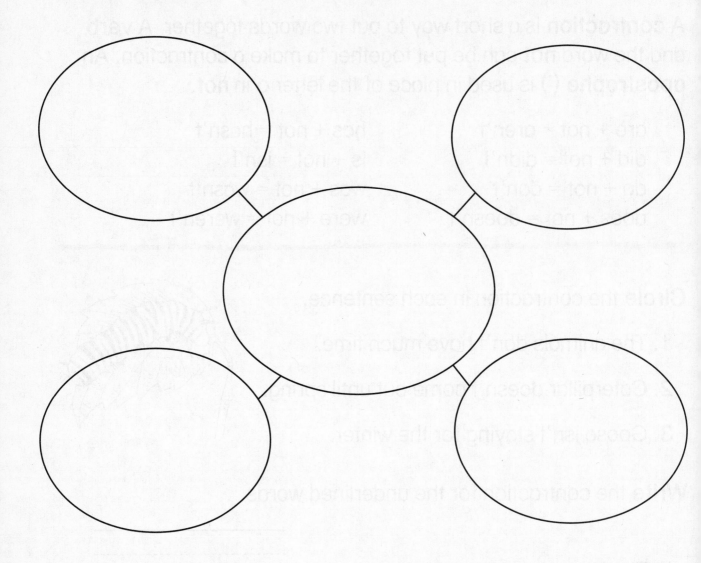

School + Home

Home Activity Your child has ideas for a play scene. Have him or her explain how actors in a play perform a story.

⊕ **1.17.A** Plan a first draft by generating ideas for writing.

Name _____

J _____ j _____

Copy the words. Write your letters the correct size.

Jack _____ Jill _____

Jake _____ jar _____

just _____ jelly _____

judge _____ jog _____

jam _____ Jon _____

wedge _____ lodge _____

jiffy _____ Jane _____

Did you write your letters the correct size? | **Yes** | **No** |

Home Activity Your child practiced writing words with *Jj* and *dge*. Have your child choose some words from the chart and use those words in a sentence.

1.21.A.1 Form upper-case letters legibly in text, using the basic conventions of print (left-to-right and top-to-bottom progression), including spacing between words and sentences. **Also 1.21.A.2.**

Name _____

Luke asked his classmates what animals they like the most. Help Luke complete the picture graph.

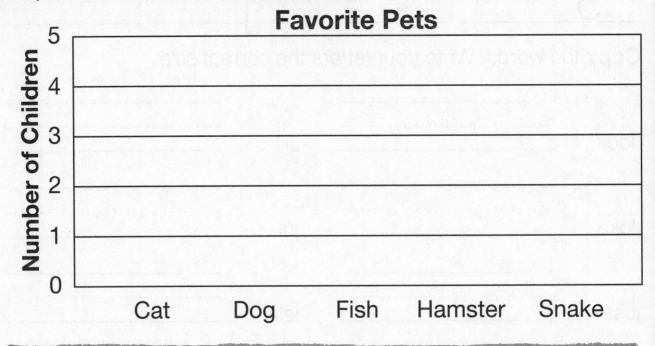

Favorite Pets

1. Five classmates like cats the most. **Draw** five cats on the picture graph.

2. Five classmates like dogs the most. **Draw** five dogs on the picture graph.

3. Three classmates like fish the most. **Draw** three fish on the picture graph.

4. Four classmates like hamsters the most. **Draw** four hamsters on the picture graph.

5. Two classmates like snakes the most. **Draw** two snakes on the picture graph.

School + Home **Home Activity** Your child learned to read and complete a picture graph. Together, make a picture graph that shows information about your favorite animals and that of your friends and family.

402 **Research** Picture Graph

✪ 1.24.C.1 Record basic information in simple visual formats. Also 1.26.A.1.

The Contest

Comparative Endings -er and -est		Consonant Pattern -dge	High-Frequency Words	
bigger	hardest	judge	have	the
harder	darkest	edge	a	is
biggest	sharpest	fudge	said	

"Let's have a contest," said Bart.

"Jess will be the judge."

"Sit on the edge, Jess."

"My fudge is darkest," said Jess.

"My pencil is sharpest."

"You're not the judge anymore!" said Bart.

Decodable Story *The Contest*
Target Skill Comparative Endings *-er* and *-est*, Consonant Pattern *-dge*

🌐 **1.3.A.1.iv.9** Decode words in context by applying common letter-sound correspondences, including: consonant digraphs including *-dge*. **Also 1.3.E.1, 1.3.H.2.**

"My plant is big," said Bart.

"My plant is bigger than that plant," said Sandy.

"Mine is the biggest," said Jess.

"See this hard trick?" said Bart.

"My trick is harder," said Sandy.

"My trick is the hardest yet," said Jess.

Name _____

Words with -er, -est

Spelling Words	High-Frequency Words
bigger biggest faster fastest taller	good-bye
tallest shorter shortest sadder saddest	before

Add -er or -est. Write the list word.

1. Tad is the tall___ boy in our class.

_____

2. The fast___ runner will win the race.

_____

3. My bat is short___ than yours.

_____

4. I need some bigg___ shoes.

_____

5. That is the sadd___ clown I've ever seen.

_____

6. You walk fast___ than I do.

_____

7. The story made her feel even sadd___.

_____

8. This is the world's bigg___ pizza.

_____

Write a word that is the opposite of each word.

_____

9. after _____   10. hello _____

Home Activity Your child wrote spelling words to complete sentences. Help your child make up a new sentence for each spelling word.

1.22.A.1 Use phonological knowledge to match sounds to letters to construct words. 1.22.C.1 Spell high-frequency words from a commonly used list.

Spelling Words with -er, -est **405**

Contractions with *Not*

Write a sentence about each season.
Use a contraction with *not* in each sentence.

Winter

_____
- -
_____

Spring

_____
- -
_____

Summer

_____
- -
_____

Fall

_____
- -
_____

School + Home

Home Activity Your child learned how to use contractions with *not* in writing. Write these sentences on paper: *He does not like winter. They do not like summer. She is not sad in the fall. We are not cold in the spring.* Have your child write the sentences using contractions with *not*.

● 1.3.G.1 Identify contractions. 1.3.G.2 Read contractions.

Name _____

Words with -er, -est

Spelling Words				
bigger	biggest	faster	fastest	taller
tallest	shorter	shortest	sadder	saddest

Finish the list words.

1. ta __ __ __ r

2. sh __ __ __ __ r

3. ta __ __ __ s

4. sh __ __ __ s

5. s __ __ d __ __

6. b __ __ __ __ t

7. b __ __ __ e

8. s __ __ __ s __

Write the missing words.

Froggy   Hopper

9. Hopper is _____ than Froggy.

10. Hopper is _____ .

fastest
faster

1.22.A.1 Use phonological knowledge to match sounds to letters to construct words.

Spelling Words with -er, -est **407**

Name _____

Contractions with *Not*

Mark the sentence that spells the contraction correctly.

1. ○ Days aren't long in the winter.
   ○ Days arent long in the winter.
   ○ Days are'nt long in the winter.

2. ○ A raccoon does'nt sleep all winter long.
   ○ A raccoon doesnt sleep all winter long.
   ○ A raccoon doesn't sleep all winter long.

3. ○ The chrysalis hasnt moved at all.
   ○ The chrysalis hasn't moved at all.
   ○ The chrysalis has'nt moved at all.

4. ○ Bears do'nt come out until spring.
   ○ Bears dont come out until spring.
   ○ Bears don't come out until spring.

5. ○ Many birds didn't stay here.
   ○ Many birds did'nt stay here.
   ○ Many birds didnt stay here.

6. ○ The fat bear was'nt hungry.
   ○ The fat bear wasn't hungry.
   ○ The fat bear wasnt hungry.

Home Activity Your child prepared for taking tests on contractions with *not*. Together read part of a short newspaper or magazine article. Take turns with your child circling contractions with *not*. Ask your child what two words make up each contraction.

⊕ **1.3.G.1** Identify contractions. **1.3.G.2** Read contractions.

Name _____

 t<u>ai</u>l →

 pl<u>ay</u>

Circle the word for each picture.

1.	2.	3.	4.
mail mall	tray tree	pal pail	pan pain

5.	6.	7.	8.
sell sail	he hay	train trap	page pay

Find the word that has the same **long a** sound as .
Mark the ⬭ to show your answer.

9. ⬭ clip
   ⬭ clap
   ⬭ clay

10. ⬭ man
    ⬭ main
    ⬭ mine

 School + Home
Home Activity Your child read words in which the long a sound is spelled *ai* and *ay,* as in *rain* and *hay.* Ask your child to name a rhyming word for each long *a* word on this page.

🌐 **1.3.A.1.v.9** Decode words in context by applying common letter-sound correspondences, including: vowel digraphs including *ay.* **Also** 1.3.A.1.v.10, 1.3.A.2.v.9, 1.3.A.2.v.10.

Phonics Vowel Digraphs *ai, ay*   **409**

Name _____

Read the words in the box.
Pick a word to complete each sentence.
Look at the scrambled letters for a hint.
Write the word on the line.

> about   enjoy   gives   surprise
> surprised   worry   would

1. I _____ helping. **nyjeo**

2. We eat at _____ 12:00. **buato**

3. _____ you please help me? **odluw**

4. Do not _____ . I will help. **woryr**

5. When we jump up, she will be _____ . **sipresrud**

6. Dad _____ us gifts. **ivseg**

7. The gifts are always a big _____ . **rrpsiues**

School + Home **Home Activity** Your child identified and read the words *about, enjoy, gives, surprise, surprised, worry,* and *would*. Ask your child to use these words to create a puppet show with paper bag puppets. Record the script on paper and have your child practice reading it aloud.

1.3.H.1 Identify at least 100 high-frequency words from a commonly used list. **Also 1.3.H.2.**

Look at the picture.
Circle the sentence that tells about the picture.

1.

Dad is happy about his new shed from Jen.
Jen is happy about her tree house from Dad.

2.

They planted a garden.

Flowers grow in gardens.

3.

We are singing in the play.
The class sets up for a play.

4.

Tom is good at running.
Tom is a good friend.

Write a sentence about the picture.

5.

_____

- - - - - - - - - - - - - - - - - - -

_____

- - - - - - - - - - - - - - - - - - -

_____

Writing · Friendly Letter

Dear Ken,

   It is almost your birthday!

What gift do you hope to get?

Do you want it to be a surprise?

Mom will take me to your party.

I will bring your gift then.

I hope you will like it.

Your friend,

Jill

Key Features of a Friendly Letter

· The letter is written to someone the writer knows.

· The letter has a polite greeting and closing.

1.19.B Write short letters that put ideas in chronological or logical sequence and use appropriate conventions (e.g., date, salutation, closing).

Name _____

Write each word correctly.
Use 's or ' at the end of each word.

Meg**'s** hat

---

1. Janes drum = _____ drum

2. dogs bone = _____ bone

3. Moms cup = _____ cup

4. babys crib = _____ crib

5. pets beds = _____ beds

Pick a word from the box to match each picture.
Write it on the line.

| girls'   Matt's |

6. _____ lunch

---

7. _____ games

School + Home

Home Activity Your child wrote words that show ownership. Point out objects in your home that are owned by one or more persons in the family. Ask your child to use a possessive to tell you who owns each object (Mike's pen).

✦ 1.3.E.1 Read base words with inflectional endings.

Words with *ai, ay*

Spelling Words				
train	way	tail	play	day
may	rain	gray	mail	afraid

Write the words in ABC order.

> tail   afraid   way   may   gray   day

1. _____

2. _____

3. _____

4. _____

5. _____

6. _____

Draw a line from the word to its picture. **Write** the word.

mail

rain

train

play

7. _____

8. _____

9. _____

10. _____

School + Home

Home Activity Your child spelled words with the long *a* sound spelled *ai* and *ay*. Have your child circle *ai* and *ay* in the spelling words.

1.22.A.1 Use phonological knowledge to match sounds to letters to construct words.

Adjectives

An **adjective** tells about a person, place, animal, or thing.

happy woman   **big** city   **loud** dog   **nice** present

Circle the adjective. **Write** the adjective on the line.
Say a sentence for each adjective.

1. heavy piñata _____

2. bright lights _____

3. hot tortillas _____

4. good friends _____

5. sweet rolls _____

 Home Activity Your child learned about adjectives. Read a story with your child. Point to a sentence and ask your child to identify any adjectives in the sentence. Continue with other sentences.

1.20.A.3 Understand and use descriptive adjectives in the context of reading, writing, and speaking.

Conventions Adjectives   **415**

Name _____

Web

Home Activity Your child is learning more about writing a letter. Have your child plan a letter to a relative.

416 **Writing** Plan

✦ **1.17.A** Plan a first draft by generating ideas for writing.

Name _____

M

m

Copy the words. Write the letters the correct size.

Meg _____

March _____

main _____

mail _____

May _____

stay _____

maid _____

chain _____

play _____

fail _____

rain _____

paid _____

Max _____

way _____

Did you write all of your letters the correct size? **Yes** **No**

Home Activity Your child practiced writing words with *Mm, ai,* and *ay*. Have your child read and copy the following sentence as neatly as he or she can. *Meg may stay and play in the rain.*

 1.21.A.1 Form upper-case letters legibly in text, using the basic conventions of print (left-to-right and top-to-bottom progression), including spacing between words and sentences. **Also 1.21.A.2.**

Find out about foods people make for celebrations.

chef

classmates

1. Who would you interview to find out foods that different families eat at celebrations?

   _____

   -

   _____

2. Who would you interview to find out how to make some of those foods?

   _____

   -

   _____

3. Write questions you would ask a local expert, such as a chef, about how to make food for a celebration.

   _____

   -

   _____

   -

   _____

   -

   _____

4. Interview a local expert using the questions you created. Share what you learned with your class.

School + Home **Home Activity** Your child learned about gathering information by interviewing people. Talk with your child about special traditions your family has for different celebrations. Ask you child to write two interview questions to ask a member of your family about the celebrations and traditions.

🌐 **1.24.A.2** Gather evidence from interviews with local experts. **Also 1.24.A.1.**

Quails

Vowel Digraphs ai, ay		Singular and Plural Possessives	High-Frequency Words	
quails	stay	birds'	are	what
main	say	farmers'	their	do
trail	may	quail's	is	one
raid	someday		the	you
gray			many	a
			live	

Quails are small, plump birds.

Quails can fly, but their main home is on land.

What do quails say?

One quail's call is *bob . . . . WHITE!*

You may see a bobwhite someday!

Decodable Story *Quails*
Target Skills Vowel Digraphs *ai, ay*; Singular and Plural Possessives

1.3.A.1.v.9 Decode words in context by applying common letter-sound correspondences, including: vowel digraphs including *ay*. **Also** 1.3.A.2.v.9, 1.3.A.1.v.10, 1.3.A.2.v.10, 1.3.E.1, 1.3.H.2.

Many quails are tan, gray, and white.

The birds' spots and stripes help them hide.

They run up the trail when foxes raid.

Quails can live on farmers' farms.

They like seeds and insects.

Farmers hope the quails will stay!

Name _____

Words with *ai, ay*

Spelling Words				
train	way	tail	play	day
may	rain	gray	mail	afraid

High-Frequency Words
about
would

Read about a dog. **Write** the missing list words.

1. I have a _____ dog.

2. He is _____ of storms.

3. He hides when it starts to _____ .

4. He barks when he hears a _____ .

5. Could he learn a _____ to play catch?

6. Could he fetch the _____ ?

7. I think he _____ learn.

8. Look at him wag his _____ .

9. I think he _____ like to play.

10. Let's think _____ training another day.

Home Activity Your child wrote spelling words to complete a story about a dog. Have your child make up a story using some of the list words.

1.22.A.1 Use phonological knowledge to match sounds to letters to construct words. 1.22.C.1 Spell high-frequency words from a commonly used list.

Spelling Words with *ai, ay* **421**

Adjectives

Write an adjective from the box to complete each sentence.

> **green   sharp   soft**

_____

1. Gina's cat has _____ fur.

2. The cat has _____ eyes.

3. Look at the cat's _____ claws.

Tell about something you like.
Use adjectives to describe it.

_____

_____

_____

_____

Choose other adjectives. **Say** a sentence for each adjective.

School + Home   **Home Activity** Your child learned how to use adjectives in writing. Take turns with your child describing what you are wearing. Have your child identify any adjectives either of you uses in your descriptions.

⊕ **1.20.A.3** Understand and use descriptive adjectives in the context of reading, writing, and speaking.

Name _____

Words with *ai, ay*

Spelling Words				
train	way	tail	play	day
may	rain	gray	mail	afraid

Underline the words that rhyme. **Write** the words.

Whose tail is on the mail?

1. _____

2. _____

Is there a train in the rain?

3. _____

4. _____

When may we play?

5. _____

6. _____

Circle the word that is spelled correctly.

7. gray   gra   8. day   dai

9. afrayd   afraid   10. waye   way

Home Activity Your child has been learning to spell words with the long *a* sound spelled *ai* and *ay*. Help your child think of and spell words that rhyme with some of the list words.

1.22.A.1 Use phonological knowledge to match sounds to letters to construct words.

Spelling Words with *ai, ay* **423**

Adjectives

Mark the sentence that has a line under the adjective.

1. ○ Grandmother reads a <u>funny</u> book.
   ○ Grandmother <u>reads</u> a funny book.
   ○ <u>Grandmother</u> reads a funny book.

2. ○ Mama <u>gave</u> Francisco a big hug.
   ○ Mama gave Francisco a <u>big</u> hug.
   ○ Mama gave Francisco a big <u>hug</u>.

3. ○ Francisco <u>made</u> a colorful piñata.
   ○ <u>Francisco</u> made a colorful piñata.
   ○ Francisco made a <u>colorful</u> piñata.

4. ○ Everyone <u>ate</u> the fresh tortillas.
   ○ Everyone ate the fresh <u>tortillas</u>.
   ○ Everyone ate the <u>fresh</u> tortillas.

5. ○ The <u>party</u> was the best present.
   ○ The party was the <u>best</u> present.
   ○ The party was the best <u>present</u>.

6. ○ Papa played a <u>long</u> song.
   ○ Papa <u>played</u> a long song.
   ○ <u>Papa</u> played a long song.

Choose other adjectives. **Say** a sentence for each adjective.

Home Activity Your child prepared for taking tests on adjectives. Together read a short, simple newspaper or magazine article. Have your child circle as many adjectives as he or she can find.

🟊 **1.20.A.3** Understand and use descriptive adjectives in the context of reading, writing, and speaking.

Name _____

Circle the word for each picture.

1.	2.	3.	4.
head herd	bride bead	sail seal	berry bread
5.	6.	7.	8.
leaf loaf	jeans jars	bake beak	clean clang

Circle the words that finish each sentence.

9. __Please/Place__ pass the __peas/bees__.

10. I __spread/spent__ the jam on the cracker.

11. I __read /rang__ my book at the __beach/birch__ yesterday.

Home Activity Your child read words in which both short e and long e sounds are spelled *ea*. Ask your child to think of rhyming words for the words on this page. Write word and review the spelling together.

1.3.A.1.v.3 Decode words in context by applying common letter-sound correspondences, including: vowel digraphs (ea). Also 1.3.A.2.v.3, 1.3.A.1.v.4, 1.3.A.2.v.4

Name _____

Read the words in the box.
Pick a word to complete each sentence.
Write the word on the line.

> draw   colors   over
> drew   great   sign   show

_____
1. Each day I like to _____ in art class.

_____
2. Ted did a _____ job on his drawing!

_____
3. I can read the _____ on the gate.

_____
4. I think red and blue are the best _____ .

_____
5. The map will _____ us the way to go.

_____
6. The frogs jump _____ the rocks.

_____
7. Last week I _____ a dog in art class.

Home Activity Your child identified and read the words *draw, colors, over, drew, great, sign,* and *show*. Have your child read each word again and make up a new sentence for each word.

1.3.H.1 Identify at least 100 high-frequency words from a commonly used list. **Also 1.3.H.2.**

Name _____

Read the story.
Follow the directions.

   One day, Penny and her mom went to East Mall. Mom wanted to get jeans for Penny. East Mall was a big mall. Penny and her mom spent a long time walking from store to store. Soon Penny wanted to go home. But her mom wanted to go to one more store. At last, they got jeans for Penny. Then they headed home. Penny went into the house first. She saw paper chains everywhere! She saw a cake. Then her friends came running and yelled, "Surprise, Penny!"

I. Circle the sentence that is the big idea of the story.

   Penny and her mom walked around a big mall.

   Penny's friends gave her a surprise birthday party.

2. Circle why you think Mom spent a long time at the mall.

   She wanted Penny's friends to get to the house before Penny.

   On that day, she wanted to spend a lot of time with Penny.

3. Write a title for this story

_____
_____
_____
_____
_____

Home Activity Your child identified the theme—the big idea—of a story. Reread the story with your child. Help your child identify the sentences in the story that helped him or her tell the big idea.

1.7 Analyze, make inferences, and draw conclusions about theme.

Comprehension Theme   **427**

Name _____

Writing • Invitation

Dear Emma,

My older brother plays soccer. He will give a free soccer lesson to kids. Please come to the lesson. It will be at my house on April 20 at 3:00 P.M. I hope you will come.

Your friend,
Kat

Key Features of an Invitation

- An invitation asks someone to an event, using polite words.

- An invitation tells important information about the event.

1.19.B Write short letters that put ideas in a chronological or logical sequence and use appropriate conventions (e.g., date, salutation, closing).

Name _____

Add -ed to each word.
Write the new word on the line.

fr**ied**

1. dry
_____

_____

2. cry
_____

_____

3. spy
_____

_____

4. worry
_____

_____

5. try
_____

_____

6. copy
_____

_____

Add -er and -est to each word.
Write the new word on the lines.

	Add -er	Add -est
7. silly		
8. funny		
9. happy		
10. easy		

Home Activity Your child practiced adding endings to words where the spelling changed from *y* to *i* before adding *-ed*, *-er*, or *-est*. Use the words above to make up a story with your child.

⊕ 1.3.E.1 Read base words with inflectional endings.

Name _____

Words with *ea*

Spelling Words				
eat	sea	each	team	please
dream	treat	beach	clean	lean

Write two list words that rhyme with the picture.

1. _____   3. _____   5. _____

2. _____   4. _____   6. _____

Write the missing words.

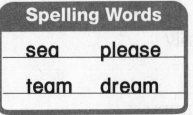

Spelling Words	
sea	please
team	dream

7. My _____ won!

8. I _____ about trips.

9. I love the _____ .

10. Can we _____ go there?

 Home Activity Your child spelled words with the long *e* sound spelled *ea*. Ask your child to name the two letters that appear in every spelling word (*ea*).

1.22.A.1 Use phonological knowledge to match sounds to letters to construct words.

Adjectives for Colors and Shapes

Some **adjectives** name colors.

white crayon   **black** pencil

Some **adjectives** name shapes.

square paper   **round** frame

Circle the adjective in each sentence that names a color or shape. **Say** a sentence for each adjective.

1. Roz has blue markers.

2. Gert has green markers.

3. Roz draws round circles.

4. Gert draws square boxes.

5. Roz adds brown dots.

6. Gert makes yellow lines.

Home Activity Your child learned about adjectives for colors and shapes. Point to objects around your home and have your child describe the objects using adjectives that name colors and shapes.

 1.20.A.3 Understand and use descriptive adjectives in the context of reading, writing, and speaking.

Conventions Adjectives for Colors and Shapes   **431**

Name _____

Web

Date

Place

Event

Time

Description

Home Activity Your child is learning about invitations. Share ideas about how people invite family members to events.

432 Writing Plan

✦ **1.17.A** Plan a first draft by generating ideas for writing.

Name _____

L | |

Copy the words. Leave the correct space between your letters.

Len _____   bead _____

lean _____   Leah _____

leap _____   leaf _____

plea _____   sea _____

seal _____   beam _____

clean _____   seat _____

leak _____   heap _____

Did you leave the correct space between your letters? Yes No

Home Activity Your child practiced writing words with *Ll* and *ea*. Have your child choose one word with *ea* and write as many rhyming words as he or she can from words on the list and not on the list.

1.21.A.1 Form upper-case letters legibly in text, using the basic conventions of print (left-to-right and top-to-bottom progression), including spacing between words and sentences. Also 1.21.A.2.

Handwriting 433

Name _____

Jordan asked her classmates which story is their favorite.
Help Jordan complete the chart.

Favorite Stories	
Goldilocks	
The Three Little Pigs	
Little Red Riding Hood	
The Tortoise and the Hare	
The Billy Goats Gruff	

||||| = 5

Make tally marks on the chart to show what Jordan learned.

I. Five classmates like **Goldilocks** the most.

2. Four classmates like **The Three Little Pigs** the most.

3. Three classmates like **Little Red Riding Hood** the most.

4. Two classmates like **The Tortoise and the Hare** the most.

5. Six classmates like **The Three Billy Goats Gruff** the most.

6. Present Jordan's results to your class by acting out the story that her classmates liked the most.

Home Activity Your child used a chart to find information, answer questions, and convey results of research. Together, make a chart showing chores that each family member does at home. Ask your child to fill in the chart as chores are completed.

1.26.A.1 Create a visual display (with adult assistance) to convey the results of the research. **Also 1.24.C.1, 1.26.A.2.**

Bread

Vowel Digraph *ea*		Adding Endings: Change *y* to *i*	High-Frequency Words	
bread	yeast	babies	a	I
eat	treat	ladies	the	is
feast	leave	dried		
wheat	meal	fried	your	
read	clean	tried	are	
beat			you	
			about	
			said	

"Babies like it! Ladies like it!

Eat it with jelly!

It's a feast in your belly!" sang
Neal.

"This is a treat!" said Beth.

"But I must leave after the
meal."

"No . . . after we clean up!" said
Neal.

Decodable Story *Bread*
Target Skills Vowel Digraph *ea*; Adding Endings: Changing *y* to *i*

1.3.A.1.v.4 Decode words in context by applying common letter-sound correspondences, including: vowel digraphs including *ea* as in *bread*. **Also** 1.3.A.1.v.3, 1.3.A.2.v.3, 1.3.A.2.v.4, **1.3.E.1, 1.3.H.2.**

"Are you singing about bread?" asked Beth.

"Yes!" said Neal. "I'm mixing wheat bread.

Will you help me?"

"I've never tried that before," said Beth.

"But I can read the card.

I'll beat in the yeast."

Name _____

Words with *ea*

Spelling Words				
eat	sea	each	team	please
dream	treat	beach	clean	lean

High-Frequency Words
colors
sign

Write the missing letters. **Write** the word.

1. Is it time to **ea**____ ?   _____

2. Let's go to the ____**ea**____ ____ .   _____

3. I can ____ ____**ea**____ the porch.   _____

4. Don't ____**ea**____ over too far.   _____

5. I had a ____**ea**____ last night.   _____

6. Will you ____ ____**ea**____ ____ sit?   _____

7. Fish live in the ____**ea** .   _____

8. My ____**ea**____ lost!   _____

9. **Write** a word that rhymes with **fine**.   _____

10. Blue, green, and red are _____.

Home Activity Your child wrote spelling words to complete sentences. Read a sentence on this page and have your child spell the list word.

⭐ 1.22.A.1 Use phonological knowledge to match sounds to letters to construct words. 1.22.C.1 Spell high-frequency words from a commonly used list.

Spelling Words with *ea* 437

Adjectives for Colors and Shapes

Color the boxes and circles.

Write about the picture.
Use color and shape words.

_____
- -
_____
_____
- -
_____
_____
- -
_____
_____
- -
_____

Choose other adjectives. **Say** a sentence for each adjective.

School + Home **Home Activity** Your child learned how to use adjectives for colors and shapes in writing. Write this sentence frame on paper: *The ___ animal runs.* Have your child write color adjectives in the sentence frame to make as many sentences as possible.

1.20.A.3 Understand and use descriptive adjectives in the context of reading, writing, and speaking.

Name _____

Words with *ea*

Write list words in the puzzle.

Spelling Words
eat
sea
each
team
please
dream
treat
beach
clean
lean

Across
2. chew food
4. not dirty

Down
1. sandy shore
3. ocean
5. thin

Draw lines through all the *i*'s and *k*'s. **Write** the word that is left.

6. t i e k a k m i _____

7. p l i e a k k s i e _____

8. k t i r e k a k i t _____

9. e i a k c i k h _____

10. d i r k i e a m _____

Home Activity Your child has been learning to spell words with the long *e* sound spelled *ea*. Have your child identify and spell the three words he or she found most difficult.

1.22.A.1 Use phonological knowledge to match sounds to letters to construct words.

Spelling Words with *ea* **439**

Adjectives for Colors and Shapes

Mark the sentence that has a line under the adjective.

1. ○ Will Cindy <u>draw</u> yellow flowers?
   ○ Will Cindy draw <u>yellow</u> flowers?
   ○ Will Cindy draw yellow <u>flowers</u>?

2. ○ She makes <u>round</u> shapes.
   ○ She <u>makes</u> round shapes.
   ○ <u>She</u> makes round shapes.

3. ○ She adds green <u>stems</u>.
   ○ She <u>adds</u> green stems.
   ○ She adds <u>green</u> stems.

4. ○ Cindy cuts <u>brown</u> paper.
   ○ Cindy <u>cuts</u> brown paper.
   ○ <u>Cindy</u> cuts brown paper.

5. ○ She pastes it on square <u>boxes</u>.
   ○ She pastes it on <u>square</u> boxes.
   ○ She <u>pastes</u> it on square boxes.

6. ○ She makes lines <u>with</u> black markers.
   ○ She makes <u>lines</u> with black markers.
   ○ She makes lines with <u>black</u> markers.

Say a sentence for each adjective. **Choose** other adjectives.

Home Activity Your child prepared for taking tests on adjectives for colors and shapes. Together read a favorite book. Have your child point out adjectives that name colors and shapes.

1.20.A.3 Understand and use descriptive adjectives in the context of reading, writing, and speaking.

Name _____

Circle the word for each picture.

 t<u>oa</u>d   bl<u>ow</u>

1.	2.	3.	4.
snap snow	road rod	boat beat	sap soap

5.	6.	7.	8.
bee bow	coat cot	ray row	leaf loaf

Write the letters that finish the words in each sentence.

9. The g _____ t drank from the b _____ l.

10. They looked high and l _____ but they could not find the

r _____ d.

School + Home **Home Activity** Your child created and read words in which the long *o* sound is spelled *oa* and *ow*, as in *toad* and *blow*. Together, list as many words as possible with the long *o* sound in their names. Then ask your child to sort the words by their spellings.

 1.3.A.1.v.7 Decode words in context by applying common letter-sound correspondences, including: vowel digraphs including *ow* as in *snow*. Also 1.3.A.2.v.7, 1.3.A.1.v.14, 1.3.A.2.v.14.

Name _____

Read the words in the box.
Pick a word to finish each sentence.
Write it in the puzzle.

> found   mouth   once   took   wild

1. You talk with your _____ .

2. "_____ upon a time . . ."

3. not lost

4. He _____ three bites
of his cake.

5. A raccoon is a _____ animal.

1.3.H.1 Identify at least 100 high-frequency words from a commonly used list. **Also 1.3.H.2.**

Name _____

Read the details.

On Friday, Michael and his father are going on a vacation. They will drive the family car to Mount Rushmore. Mount Rushmore is in South Dakota. It is a mountain with the faces of four American presidents carved into it. Michael and his father will camp nearby. They will have a lot of fun.

Circle the details that are from the story you just read.

1. Michael and his father are going on vacation.

   Michael and his father will fly.

   Mount Rushmore is in North Dakota.

   Michael and his father will camp.

   Michael and his father will drive.

Write two facts about the story.

_____
2._____
_____
_____
_____
_____
_____

School + Home **Home Activity** Your child has learned to identify facts and details from a story. Read a story with your child and point out facts and details.

1.4.B.7 Locate facts about other texts. **Also 1.4.B.3, 1.4.B.4, 1.4.B.8, 1.14.B.1, 1.14.B.2.**

Comprehension Facts and Details   **443**

Writing • Descriptive Poem

 The Farm

We hop on the big yellow school bus.

To the farm it takes us.

Cows, pigs, and sheep we see!

But the best part of all

is watching the farmer haul

huge bales of hay

to the barn where the animals stay.

Key Features of a Descriptive Poem

- Most descriptive poems are shorter than a story.

- Lines in a descriptive poem can either rhyme or not rhyme.

1.18.B.1 Write short poems that convey sensory details.

Name _____

Circle the word for each picture.

1.

stub
scrub

2.

splash
slash

3.

squeeze
sneeze

4.

sting
string

5.

lint
splint

6.

spring
sing

7.

those
three

8.

stripe
ripe

Write the letters that finish the words in each sentence.

9. She _____ e w the ball _____ o u g h the

_____ e e n door.

10. I had a sore _____ o a t.

School + Home **Home Activity** Your child created and read words that begin with three-letter consonant blends. Have your child draw pictures of *screen, spray, squint,* and *street.* Have him or her label each picture with the word.

1.3.B.1 Combine sounds from letters to create recognizable words.

Phonics Three-Letter Consonant Blends   **445**

Words with *oa, ow*

Read the clues. **Write** the word.

It rhymes with **willow**.
You sleep on it.

_____

1. _____

It rhymes with **mow**.
It's cold and white.

_____

3. _____

It rhymes with **load**.
Cars go on it.

_____

5. _____

It rhymes with **goat**.
It goes in water.

_____

2. _____

It rhymes with **fellow**.
It's a color.

_____

4. _____

It rhymes with **goat**.
You wear it.

_____

6. _____

Spelling Words
boat
road
snow
row
yellow
loaf
coat
soap
blow
pillow

Write the missing word.

7. I like to ____ bubbles.

8. Did you ____ the boat?

9. I got ____ in my eyes.

10. The ____ of bread is warm.

© Pearson Education, Inc., 1

Home Activity Your child spelled words with the long *o* vowel sound spelled *oa* and *ow*. Have your child underline *oa* and *ow* in the spelling words.

1.22.A.1 Use phonological knowledge to match sounds to letters to construct words.

Adjectives for Sizes

Some **adjectives** describe size. Words such as **big, small, long,** and **short** describe size.

small bird

big bird

Circle each adjective that describes size.
Say a sentence for each adjective.

1. big bus

2. long river

3. little fish

4. short stripes

5. tall window

6. huge flag

Home Activity Your child learned about adjectives for sizes. Point to objects around your home. Ask your child if the object is big or small (tall or short, long or short). Have your child answer using the adjective in a sentence.

1.20.A.3 Understand and use descriptive adjectives in the context of reading, writing, and speaking.

Conventions Adjectives for Sizes   **447**

Name _____

Writing · Poem

A Place and What You See

Home Activity Your child can plan a poem that describes a place. Look at pictures of a place with your child. Describe it.

1.17.A Plan a first draft by generating ideas for writing.

Name _____

F _____   f _____

Copy the words. Write the letters from left to right.

Flo   _____   Fred   _____

float   _____   goat   _____

boat   _____   grow   _____

flow   _____   foam   _____

loaf   _____   throat   _____

road   _____   blow   _____

moan   _____   slow   _____

Did you write all of your letters from left to right? | **Yes** | | **No** |

School + Home   **Home Activity** Your child practiced writing words with *Ff, ow,* and *oa.* Have your child read and write any five words from the list one more time.

1.21.A.1 Form upper-case letters legibly in text, using the basic conventions of print (left-to-right and top-to-bottom progression), including spacing between words and sentences. **Also 1.21.A.2.**

Name _____

Ray asked his friends about their favorite American treasures. Help Ray complete the bar graph.

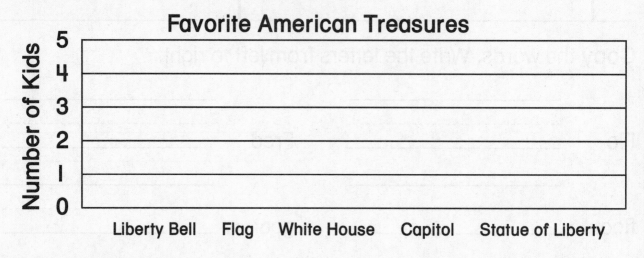

Favorite American Treasures

Number of Kids

5
4
3
2
1
0

Liberty Bell   Flag   White House   Capitol   Statue of Liberty

---

Make bars on the graph to show what Ray learned.

1. Three friends like the Liberty Bell the most.

2. Four friends like the American Flag the most.

3. Two friends like the White House the most.

4. One friend likes the Capitol the most.

5. Five friends like the Statue of Liberty the most.

6. Present Ray's results to your class by dramatizing the American treasure that his friends liked the most.

School + Home **Home Activity** Your child learned how to make and read a bar graph. Help your child poll family members and friends about their favorite places to visit. Make a bar graph to record the results.

1.24.C.1 Record basic information in a simple visual format. **Also 1.26.A.1.**

It's Spring!

Vowel Digraphs oa, ow			3-Letter Consonant Blends, Including *thr, spl*		High-Frequency Words	
toad	snow	show	spring	thrill	the	a
croaks	crow	throw	splash	street	what	your
boat	flowers	yellow	sprout		do	out
goat	row		stream		you	is
oats	grow		stretch		to	

The snow went away. It's spring!

The crow flies. The toad croaks.

The fish splash. The flowers sprout.

Spring is a thrill!

Spring is the best season on my street . . . until summer, that is!

Decodable Story *It's Spring!*
Target Skills Vowel Digraphs *oa, ow*; 3-Letter Consonant Blends, Including *thr, spl*

1.3.A.1.v.7 Decode words in context by applying common letter-sound correspondences, including: vowel digraphs including *ow* as in *snow*. **Also 1.3.A.2.v.7, 1.3.A.1.v.14, 1.3.A.2.v.14, 1.3.A.1.iii, 1.3.A.2.iii, 1.3.H.2.**

What do you like to do in spring?

You can row a boat up the stream.

You can grow a rose.

You can throw a ball to a pal.

You can feed oats to the goat.

You can stretch out on the grass.

Words with *oa, ow*

Spelling Words					High-Frequency Words
boat	road	snow	row	yellow	wild
loaf	coat	soap	blow	pillow	once

Write the missing list word.

_____

1. Lemons are _____ .

2. Wash with _____ .

3. Would you like to ride in our _____ ?

4. I sleep on a soft _____ .

5. Wear your _____ .

6. He will _____ the boat.

7. Please buy a _____ of bread.

8. Is it cold enough to _____ ?

9. I took this road _____ .

10. The monkey is a _____ animal.

Home Activity Your child wrote spelling words to complete sentences. Ask your child to create a sentence using one or two of the spelling words.

1.22.A.1 Use phonological knowledge to match sounds to letters to construct words. 1.22.C.1 Spell high-frequency words from a commonly used list.

Spelling Words with *oa, ow* 453

Adjectives for Sizes

Write about something you like that is very big.
It might be an animal, a place, or a thing.
Use adjectives to tell about it.

_____

_____

_____

_____

Write about something you like that is very small.
It might be an animal, a place, or a thing.
Use adjectives to tell about it. **Say** the adjectives you used.

_____

_____

_____

_____

_____

Home Activity Your child learned how to use adjectives for sizes in writing. Point to pictures that show big, small, long, short, and tall things, one at a time. Ask: *What size is the ___?* Have your child answer the question.

1.20.A.3 Understand and use descriptive adjectives in the context of reading, writing, and speaking.

Name _____

Words with *oa, ow*

Spelling Words				
boat	road	snow	row	yellow
loaf	coat	soap	blow	pillow

Write the list word that belongs in the group.

blanket   sheet
----
1. _____

rain   sleet
----
2. _____

blue   red
----
3. _____

street   highway
----
4. _____

jacket   sweater
----
5. _____

ship   ocean liner
----
6. _____

Circle the word that matches. **Write** it.

7. row   bow   row

8. loaf   load   loaf

9. blow   blow   flow

10. soap   soak   soap

Home Activity Your child has been learning words with the long *o* vowel sound spelled *oa* and *ow*. Give clues about a word. Can your child guess and spell the word?

⭐ 1.22.A.1 Use phonological knowledge to match sounds to letters to construct words.

Adjectives for Sizes

Mark the sentence that has a line under the adjective.

1. ○ We <u>saw</u> a big bus.
   ○ We saw a big <u>bus</u>.
   ○ We saw a <u>big</u> bus.

2. ○ Look at the <u>huge</u> house.
   ○ <u>Look</u> at the huge house.
   ○ Look at the huge <u>house</u>.

3. ○ A long river <u>flows</u> by the road.
   ○ A <u>long</u> river flows by the road.
   ○ A long <u>river</u> flows by the road.

4. ○ The bird <u>has</u> a small fish.
   ○ The <u>bird</u> has a small fish.
   ○ The bird has a <u>small</u> fish.

5. ○ The fish has a <u>short</u> tail.
   ○ The <u>fish</u> has a short tail.
   ○ The fish has a short <u>tail</u>.

6. ○ A little bird was in the <u>sky</u>.
   ○ A <u>little</u> bird was in the sky.
   ○ A little bird <u>was</u> in the sky.

Choose other adjectives. **Say** a sentence for each adjective.

Home Activity Your child prepared for taking tests on adjectives for sizes. Together read a favorite storybook. Have your child find adjectives for sizes.

1.20.A.3 Understand and use descriptive adjectives in the context of reading, writing, and speaking.

Name _____

Circle the word for each picture.

1.	**2.**	**3.**	**4.**
night note	sit lie	tie tea	fit fight
5.	**6.**	**7.**	**8.**
pit pie	hay high	sit sight	tight toad

Read the sentences.
Circle the words that have the **long i** sound spelled **ie** and **igh**.
Underline the words that have the **long e** sound spelled **ie**.

9. I would like another piece of birthday cake.

10. He believes that he is right.

11. I am sorry that I lied to you.

School + Home   **Home Activity** Your child practiced reading words in which the long *i* sound is spelled *igh* and *ie* as in *light* and *pie*, and words in which the long *e* sound is spelled *ie*. Encourage your child to create a poem, nonsense rhyme, or song using *igh* and *ie* words.

🌐 **1.3.A.1.v.15** Decode words in context by applying common letter-sound correspondences, including: vowel digraphs including *ie* as in *chief*. Also **1.3.A.2.v.15, 1.3.A.1.v.16, 1.3.A.2.v.16, 1.3.A.1.v.17, 1.3.A.2.v.17.**

Name _____

Read the words in the box.
Pick a word to match each clue.
Write it on the line.

> above   eight   laugh   moon   touch

1.
   "Ha, ha, ha!" _____

2.
   five, six, seven, _____

3.
   not below _____

4.
   feel _____

5.
   stars, planets, _____

School + Home

Home Activity Your child identified and read the words *above, eight, laugh, moon,* and *touch.* Act out clues for each word and have your child guess which word you picked.

1.3.H.1 Identify at least 100 high-frequency words from a commonly used list. **Also 1.3.H.2.**

Name _____

Read the story.

Nina and Anna are best friends. On Sunday, they will go to camp for one week. They will sleep in a tent. They will meet other girls. They will go swimming. At night they can watch the moon and the stars. Nina and Anna will have a good time.

Read the details. **Circle** the details that are from the story.

They will sleep in tents.

They will go swimming.

They will look for shells.

Camp is a long way from their home.

At night they will watch the moon and the stars.

Write two facts about the story.

_____
_____
_____
_____
_____
_____
_____
_____

Home Activity Your child has learned to identify facts and details from a story. Read a story with your child and ask your child to name one detail and one fact from the story.

1.4.B.7. Locate facts about other texts. **Also** 1.4.B.3, 1.4.B.4, 1.4.B.8, 1.14.B.1, 1.14.B.2.

Comprehension Facts and Details **459**

Name _____

Writing Prompt: Write a story about a child who rides a horse.

 Riley's Ride

  Riley went with her family to the fair. There were horses there. Could she ride one? Riley's mom paid for a ride. Riley got to ride a horse. She picked a black and white horse. They went in circles around the field. It was fun!

1.18.A Write brief stories that include a beginning, middle, and end.

Name _____

Circle the word for each picture.

__kn__ight   __wr__ench

1.
knife   night

2.
rest   wrist

3.
nine   knit

4.
knob   not

5.
note   knot

6.
wreck   rack

7.
white   write

8.
ring   wrong

Find the word that has the same beginning sound as the picture.
Mark the ⬭ to show your answer.

9. ⬭ wren
   ⬭ when
   ⬭ went

10. ⬭ sneak
    ⬭ kite
    ⬭ knock

Home Activity Your child read words that begin with *kn* as in *knight* and *wr* as in *wrench*. Have your child copy all the words from the page that begin with *kn* and *wr* and ask him or her to circle the silent letter in each word.

✪ **1.3.A.1.iv.8** Decode words in context by applying common letter-sound correspondences, including: consonant digraphs including *kn*.
Also 1.3.A.2.iv.8.

Name _____

Words with *ie, igh*

Spelling Words				
lie	tie	high	might	right
night	bright	light	pie	tight

Write the list word that names the picture.

1. _____ 2. _____ 3. _____

Write the list word that means the same as the underlined word.

4. These gloves are too <u>snug</u>.

4. _____

5. What is the <u>correct</u> answer?

5. _____

6. The wall is <u>tall</u>.

6. _____

7. We pulled with all our <u>strength</u>.

7. _____

8. Let's wait until <u>evening</u>.

8. _____

9. She is very <u>smart</u>.

9. _____

10. I would not tell a <u>fib</u>.

10. _____

Home Activity Your child spelled words with the long *i* sound spelled *ie* and *igh*. Have your child circle *ie* and *igh* in the spelling words.

1.22.A.1 Use phonological knowledge to match sounds to letters to construct words.

Name _____

Adjectives for What Kind

An **adjective** can tell what kind.

warm day

pretty flowers

Write the adjective that tells what kind.
Say a sentence for each adjective.

1. loud cattle

_____

2. happy cows

_____

3. hot sun

_____

4. bright lights

_____

5. tall tree

_____

6. dark skies

_____

School + Home

Home Activity Your child learned about adjectives for what kind. Write *hot, cold, dry* in one list and the nouns *snow, sun, socks* in another list. Ask your child to combine the adjectives and nouns (*hot sun, cold snow, dry socks*).

1.20.A.3 Understand and use descriptive adjectives in the context of reading, writing, and speaking.

Name _____

Realistic Story
Top Score Response

Focus/Ideas	A good realistic story clearly tells what characters do.
Organization	A good realistic story has a beginning, middle, and end.
Voice	A good realistic story shows the writer's and characters' feelings.
Word Choice	A good realistic story uses words that describe characters, setting, and events.
Sentences	A good realistic story has different kinds of sentences that are clear and complete.
Conventions	A good realistic story uses adjectives that tell what kind.

Home Activity Your child is writing a story about children at a ranch. Share ideas about ranches in stories, movies, or experience.

1.17 Use elements of the writing process to compose text.
1.17.B Develop drafts by sequencing ideas through writing sentences.

Name _____

Z

z

Copy the words. Write your letters the correct size.

Zeke _____

high _____

buzz _____

fizz _____

tie _____

fried _____

sigh _____

fuzz _____

cried _____

lie _____

flies _____

Zena _____

sight _____

light _____

Did you write all of your letters the correct size? | **Yes** | **No** |

School + Home

Home Activity Your child practiced writing words with *Zz*, *ie*, and *igh*. Have your child find three words from the list that rhyme with *sigh* and write them one more time. *(high, tie, lie)*

⊕ **1.21.A.1** Form upper-case letters legibly in text, using the basic conventions of print (left-to-right and top-to-bottom progression), including spacing between words and sentences. **Also 1.21.A.2.**

Name _____

Read the guide words.
Write the word from the box that
you would find on that page.

tag bed hand hot cat

1. hat hunt

   _____
   - - - - - - - - - - - -
   _____

2. bag box

   _____
   - - - - - - - - - - - -
   _____

3. book cut

   _____
   - - - - - - - - - - - -
   _____

4. sack tend

   _____
   - - - - - - - - - - - -
   _____

dog feed gone lip mint

5. let lock

   _____
   - - - - - - - - - - - -
   _____

6. day duck

   _____
   - - - - - - - - - - - -
   _____

7. gas gust

   _____
   - - - - - - - - - - - -
   _____

8. man mole

   _____
   - - - - - - - - - - - -
   _____

School + Home **Home Activity** Your child learned about using alphabetical order and guide words in a dictionary. Look through a children's dictionary with your child. Make a game of finding new words by using the guide words at the top of each page.

🌐 **1.24.B.1** Use text features in age-appropriate reference works to locate information. **Also 1.23.B.1.**

The Gift

Vowel Digraphs ie, igh		Consonant Patterns kn, wr		High-Frequency Words	
brief	might	knee	wrench	a	were
chief	right	kneeled	wrapped	the	is
necktie	bright	knot		was	what
ties	tight	know		to	do
tie	sighed	wrong		said	too
night					

Carl went on a brief shopping trip.

The chief reason was to get a gift.

His dad's birthday party was that night.

Carl didn't know what to do.

Then he got a wrench instead.

He wrapped it. Dad liked it!

4

Decodable Story *The Gift*
Target Skills Vowel Digraphs *ie, igh*; Consonant Patterns *kn, wr*

1.3.A.1.v.15 Decode words in context by applying common letter-sound correspondences, including: vowel digraphs including *ie* as in *chief*. **Also** 1.3.A.2.v.15, 1.3.A.1.v.16, 1.3.A.2.v.16, 1.3.A.1.v.17, 1.3.A.2.v.17, 1.3.H.2.

"Dad might like a necktie," said Carl.

The ties were right by his knee.

Carl kneeled to see.

Carl tried on a bright red tie.

He made the knot too tight.

"This is all wrong!" he sighed.

Name _____

Words with *ie, igh*

Spelling Words				
lie	tie	high	might	right
night	bright	light	pie	tight

High-Frequency Words
above
laugh

Write a list word to finish the sentence.

1. You are r____.

2. Turn on the l____.

3. I love to eat p____!

4. Will you wear a t____?

5. The roof is h____.

6. It's a cold n____.

7. The stars are b____.

8. My belt is too t____.

9. Do not l____ at us.

10. The sign is a____ the school.

1. _____

2. _____

3. _____

4. _____

5. _____

6. _____

7. _____

8. _____

9. _____

10. _____

Home Activity Your child wrote spelling words to complete sentences. Help your child use the list words in new sentences.

1.22.A.1 Use phonological knowledge to match sounds to letters to construct words. 1.22.C.1 Spell high-frequency words from a commonly used list.

Spelling Words with *ie, igh* **469**

Name _____

Adjectives for What Kind

Write about something your family does
on a holiday.
Use adjectives such as *loud, tasty,*
or *cold* to tell about it.

_____

_____

_____

_____

_____

_____

_____

_____

_____

_____

_____

_____

Choose other adjectives. **Say** a sentence for each adjective.

Home Activity Your child learned how to use adjectives for what kind in writing. With your child, look
through a family photo album. Talk about what you see in photos using adjectives that tell what kind.

470 Conventions Adjectives for What Kind

1.20.A.3 Understand and use descriptive adjectives in the
context of reading, writing, and speaking.

Name _____

Words with *ie, igh*

Draw a line through three rhyming list words
in a row. **Write** the words.

might	read	lie
row	tie	tight
pie	loaf	road

pie	right	coat
sled	tight	low
blue	might	high

Spelling Words

lie
tie
high
might
right
night
bright
light
pie
tight

1. _____
  ----
2. _____
  ----
3. _____
  ----
4. _____
  ----
5. _____
  ----
6. _____

Write the missing words.

_____
  ----

7. It is up _____ .

8. It looks _____ .

9. You see it at _____ .

10. It looks like a _____ .

night	bright
light	high

School + Home

Home Activity Your child has been learning to spell words with the long *i* sound spelled *ie* and *igh*. Say a
list word. Ask your child how the long *i* sound is spelled (*ie* or *igh*).

1.22.A.1 Use phonological knowledge to match sounds to letters
to construct words.

Name _____

Adjectives for What Kind

Mark the sentence that has a line under the adjective.

1. ○ <u>Dinner</u> on Sunday is a great meal.
   ○ Dinner on <u>Sunday</u> is a great meal.
   ○ Dinner on Sunday is a <u>great</u> meal.

2. ○ A ranch hand bakes <u>fresh</u> bread.
   ○ A ranch hand <u>bakes</u> fresh bread.
   ○ A ranch hand bakes fresh <u>bread.</u>

3. ○ Another ranch hand makes spicy <u>stew.</u>
   ○ Another ranch hand makes <u>spicy</u> stew.
   ○ Another ranch hand <u>makes</u> spicy stew.

4. ○ I pour glasses of <u>cold</u> milk.
   ○ I <u>pour</u> glasses of cold milk.
   ○ I pour <u>glasses</u> of cold milk.

5. ○ Sweet oranges <u>are</u> our dessert.
   ○ <u>Sweet</u> oranges are our dessert.
   ○ Sweet <u>oranges</u> are our dessert.

6. ○ <u>We</u> wash the dirty dishes together.
   ○ We <u>wash </u>the dirty dishes together.
   ○ We wash the <u>dirty</u> dishes together.

Choose other adjectives. **Say** a sentence for each adjective.

School + Home **Home Activity** Your child prepared for taking tests on adjectives for what kind. Together read a short, simple newspaper or magazine article. Have your child circle adjectives that tell what kind.

✪ **1.20.A.3** Understand and use descriptive adjectives in the context of reading, writing, and speaking.

Name _____

Pick a word from the box to finish each compound word.
Write it on the line.
Draw a line to the picture it matches.

flashlight

| boat   man   paper   watch |

1. news _____

2. row _____

3. wrist _____

4. snow _____

Find the compound word.
Mark the ⬭ to show your answer.

5. ⬭ raining
   ⬭ rainy
   ⬭ raincoat

6. ⬭ popcorn
   ⬭ puppy
   ⬭ popping

7. ⬭ mitten
   ⬭ marching
   ⬭ backpack

8. ⬭ balloon
   ⬭ daydream
   ⬭ broken

School + Home   **Home Activity** Your child read compound words—words formed by joining two or more words. Have your child tell what two words make up these compound words: *rainbow, snowflake, peanut, baseball, backpack.*

🟊 1.3.F.1. Use knowledge of the meaning of base words to identify common compound words. **Also 1.3.F.2.**

Phonics Compound Words   **473**

Name _____

Read the words in the box.
Pick a word to finish each sentence.
Write it on the line.

| picture   remember   room   stood   thought   would |

1. Mom took a _____ of my friends and me.

2. We _____ by a tree.

3. I _____ the picture was wonderful.

4. I will hang the picture in my _____ .

5. It will help me _____ my friends.

School + Home

Home Activity Your child learned to identify and read the words *picture, remember, room, stood,* and *thought.* Write each word on a small piece of paper. Say each word. Have your child put the words in the order in which you read them and then repeat the words in a different order.

474 **High-Frequency Words**

© Pearson Education, Inc., 1

1.3.H.1 Identify at least 100 high-frequency words from a commonly used list. **Also 1.3.H.2.**

Name _____

Read the story.
Underline the answer to each question.

Popcorn is a very old food. People in many lands planted popcorn. They found out something about this corn. Heat would make it pop! Other corns would not pop. The popped corn looked like snowflakes. Some people wore strings of it around their necks or on their heads. These people also ate the popped corn. Other people ate popcorn in a bowl with milk.

1. What is the story all about?

   popcorn   snowflakes

2. What is the big idea of the story?

   Long ago, people found many uses for popcorn.

   People can wear strings of popped popcorn.

3. Why do you think some people wore strings of popcorn?

   They liked the color of the popped corn.

   They liked the snowflake shape of the popped corn.

Home Activity Your child identified the theme—the big idea—of a story. Reread the story with your child. Have your child underline the sentences in the story that helped him or her tell the big idea.

1.7 Analyze, make inferences, and draw conclusions about theme.

Comprehension Theme **475**

Name _____

Writing • Thank-You Note

Dear Hunter,

Thank you for sharing your basketball with me.
I had fun playing two games with you.

Your friend,
Cody

Key Features of a Thank-You Note

· A thank-you note thanks someone for doing
something nice.

· It tells how the writer feels.

School + Home

Home Activity Your child is learning about writing a thank-you note. Discuss ways of expressing thanks.

476 Writing Thank-You Note

1.19.B Write short letters that put ideas in a chronological
or logical sequence and use appropriate conventions (e.g., date,
salutation, closing).

Name _____

Circle the word for each picture.

1.	2.	3.	4.
blew black	flow flew	glue glow	chick chew

5.	6.	7.	8.
sit suit	stew stop	joke juice	news nose

Read the words in the box.
Pick a word to finish each sentence.

> **bruise   drew   true**

9. It is _____ that I love ice cream.

10. He has a _____ on his leg.

11. My sister _____ this picture.

 School + Home **Home Activity** Your child practiced reading words with *ew*, *ue*, and *ui* as in *blew*, *glue*, and *suit*. Work with your child to make up silly rhyming pairs that contain this vowel sound and these spellings, such as *blue stew* or *fruit suit*.

1.3.A.1.v.13 Decode words in context by applying common letter-sound correspondences, including: vowel digraphs including *ew*. **Also 1.3.A.2.v.13.**

Phonics Vowel Digraphs *ew, ue, ui*   **477**

Name _____

Compound Words

Write the list word that names the picture.

backpack

outside

baseball

herself

flashlight

bluebird

lunchbox

suitcase

inside

brainstorm

1. _____

2. _____

3. _____

4. _____

5. _____

6. _____

Write the last part of the compound word.
Write the compound word.

7. in _____

8. her _____

9. brain _____

10. out _____

Home Activity Your child spelled compound words. Have your child name the two words in each compound word.

478 Spelling Compound Words

1.22.A.1 Use phonological knowledge to match sounds to letters to construct words.

Name _____

Adjectives for How Many and Articles

Some **adjectives** tell how many. The adjectives **a, an,** and **the** are called **articles**.

three dogs

the baby

Draw lines to match the words to the pictures.
Say each adjective in a sentence.

1. two cribs

2. four chairs

3. five pictures

4. three boys

5. a house

School + Home

Home Activity Your child learned about adjectives for how many. Read a counting story with your child. Have your child point out the adjectives that tell how many and use his or her fingers to show how many each adjective describes.

1.20.A.3 Understand and use descriptive adjectives in the context of reading, writing, and speaking.

Name _____

Letter Format

Dear _____ ,

_____

_____

_____

_____

_____

_____

_____

_____

_____

_____

_____

_____

_____

_____ ,

_____

_____

1.17.A Plan a first draft by generating ideas for writing.

Name _____

1   2   3   4   5

Trace and **write** the numbers.

1

2

3

4

5

Circle your best number in each line.

Copy the sentence. Leave the correct space between words.

Sue has a new blue suit.

Home Activity Your child practiced writing numbers 1, 2, 3, 4, 5 and sentences with words with *ew, ui,* and *eu.* Have your child practice writing the numbers one more time. Then write the following words on a sheet of paper and have your child rewrite them to make a sentence: *knew, I, was, it, and true. (I knew it was true.)*

1.21.A.1 Form upper-case letters legibly in text, using the basic conventions of print (left-to-right and top-to-bottom progression), including spacing between words and sentences. **Also 1.21.A.2.**

Handwriting 481

Name _____

Alan sent this e-mail to his friends.
Help Alan record what he learned.

○○○

From: Alan
Subject: Your favorite treasure
Date: April 4

I want to find out your favorite treasure.

Please tell me what your favorite treasure is.

Favorite Treasures	
Stuffed Animal	
Blanket	
Favorite Toy	
Gift from a Relative	

⊦⊦⊦⊦ = 5

Make tally marks to show what Alan learned.

1. Five friends treasure a stuffed animal.

2. Three friends treasure a blanket.

3. Four friends treasure a favorite toy.

4. Seven friends treasure a gift from a relative.

Home Activity Your child learned how to write, send, and reply to an e-mail. If possible, help your child compose and send an e-mail to a family member.

⊕ **1.24.A.1** Gather evidence from available sources (natural). **Also 1.23.B.1.**

Sue's Daydream

Compound Words		Vowel Digraphs *ue, ew, ui*		High-Frequency Words	
daydream	sunlight	Sue	crew	was	I
daydreaming	inside	true	Drew	a	to
onto	popcorn	blue	juice	the	
suitcase	everyone	new	cruise	they	
into	herself	flew		said	

Sue was in reading class,

but she wasn't reading.

It's true—Sue was daydreaming!

"Time for math!" said Miss Drew.

"I must quit daydreaming," Sue said to herself.

"But a cruise might be fun . . ."

Decodable Story *Sue's Daydream*
Target Skills Compound Words; Vowel Digraphs *ue, ew, ui*

1.3.F2 Use knowledge of the meaning of base words to read common compound words.
Also 1.3.A.1.v.13, 1.3.A.2.v.13, 1.3.H.2.

She got onto a plane with her
new suitcase.

The plane flew off into the blue
sky.

Sunlight streamed in.

The crew inside was nice.

"We've got juice and popcorn for
everyone," they said.

Name _____

Compound Words

Spelling Words				
backpack	outside	baseball	herself	flashlight
bluebird	lunchbox	suitcase	inside	brainstorm

Read about some good friends. **Write** the missing list words.

High-Frequency Words
remember
picture

1. Ellie and I went o_____ .

2. Ellie had a f_____ .

3. We saw b_____ feathers.

4. We looked i_____ a hollow tree.

5. Next, we played b_____ .

6. Then we got a snack out of my l_____ .

7. We got juice out of Ellie's b_____ .

8. Ellie drank three boxes of juice by h_____ .

9. I still p_____ Ellie and the juice.

10. It is fun to r_____ her.

Home Activity Your child used spelling words to complete a story about friends. Ask your child to tell about a friend, using some of the list words.

1.22.A.1 Use phonological knowledge to match sounds to letters to construct words. 1.22.C.1 Spell high-frequency words from a commonly used list.

Spelling Compound Words **485**

Adjectives for How Many and Articles

Look at the picture. **Complete** each sentence with
an adjective from the box. **Say** a sentence for each article.

(a   two   three)

1. There are _____ people in this family.

2. There are _____ children.

3. There is _____ man.

Write about the people in your family.
Use adjectives that tell how many.

_____

_____

_____

_____

_____

_____

Home Activity Your child learned how to use adjectives for how many in writing. Place groups of one, two, three, four, and five pennies on a table and have your child write sentences about the groups using adjectives that tell how many.

Name _____

Compound Words

Connect two parts to make a list word.
Write the compound word.

1. in   storm   1. _____

2. her   side   2. _____

3. brain   light   3. _____

4. flash   self   4. _____

5. suit   bird   5. _____

6. blue   case   6. _____

Spelling Words

backpack
outside
baseball
herself
flashlight
bluebird
lunchbox
suitcase
inside
brainstorm

Circle the word that is spelled correctly.

7. lunchbox   lonchbox   8. owtside   outside

9. backpack   back pack   10. basball   baseball

School + Home   **Home Activity** Your child has been learning to spell compound words. Help your child brainstorm other compound words.

⊕ **1.22.A.1** Use phonological knowledge to match sounds to letters to construct words.

Spelling Compound Words   **487**

Adjectives for How Many and Articles

Mark the sentence that has a line under the adjective.

1. ○ There are <u>ten</u> families in the park.
   ○ There are ten <u>families</u> in the park.
   ○ There are ten families in the <u>park</u>.

2. ○ Four brothers <u>throw</u> a football.
   ○ Four brothers throw a <u>football</u>.
   ○ <u>Four</u> brothers throw a football.

3. ○ I see three <u>fathers</u> on a bench.
   ○ I see <u>three</u> fathers on a bench.
   ○ I <u>see</u> three fathers on a bench.

4. ○ Where <u>are</u> my two sisters?
   ○ Where are my two <u>sisters</u>?
   ○ Where are my <u>two</u> sisters?

5. ○ <u>Six</u> children play tag on the grass.
   ○ Six children <u>play</u> tag on the grass.
   ○ Six children play tag on the <u>grass</u>.

6. ○ There are five <u>mothers</u> with babies.
   ○ There are <u>five</u> mothers with babies.
   ○ There are five mothers with <u>babies</u>.

Choose other adjectives. **Say** a sentence for each adjective.

Home Activity Your child prepared for taking tests on adjectives for how many. Together read a short, simple newspaper or magazine article. Have your child circle adjectives that tell how many.

⊕ **1.20.A.3** Understand and use descriptive adjectives in the context of reading, writing, and speaking.

Name _____

Add -ly or **-ful** to the word in ( ).
Write the new word on the line.   nice + -ly = nice**ly**

(play)

_____

- -

I. The dog is _____ .

(slow)

_____

- -

2. The dog walked _____ .

(quick)

_____

- -

3. Then it ran _____ !

(safe)

_____

- -

4. The dog got home _____ .

(thank)

_____

- -

5. Miss Moon was _____ .

School + Home **Home Activity** Your child added *-ly* and *-ful* to words. Ask your child to give you instructions using words with the *-ly* suffix, such as *Clap loudly; Talk softly; Walk quickly.* Follow the instructions. Then have your child write simple sentences using *playful* and *thankful*.

Name _____

Read the words in the box.
Pick a word to match each clue.
Write it on the line.

| across   because   dance   only   opened   shoes   told |

1.

_____
- - - - - - - - - - - - - - - - -
_____

2.

_____
- - - - - - - - - - - - - - - - -
_____

3.

_____
- - - - - - - - - - - - - - - - -
_____

4. She said, "I _____ you to read slowly."

_____
- - - - - - - - - - - - - - - - -
_____

---

5. The plant grows _____ it has water.

_____
- - - - - - - - - - - - - - - - -
_____

6. Mom said, "_____ one treat!"

_____
- - - - - - - - - - - - - - - - -
_____

7.

_____
- - - - - - - - - - - - - - - - -
_____

Home Activity Your child learned to read the words *across, because, dance, only, opened, shoes,* and *told.* Make up more clues for the words on this page. Ask your child to identify the words. Challenge your child to think of some clues.

1.3.H.1. Identify at least 100 high-frequency words from a commonly used list. **Also 1.3.H.2.**

Name _____

Draw a line to match what happens with why it happens.

What Happens	Why It Happens

1.

2.

3.

4.

5.

RC-1.D.1 Make inferences about text. **Also RC-1.D.2.**

Comprehension Cause and Effect **491**

Name _____

Writing · Directions

How to Make a Drum

First, get a coffee can with a plastic lid.

Next, color a piece of paper.

Wrap it around the coffee can.

Then give it to your friend.

See who can drum the loudest!

Key Features of Directions

· Directions give details about how to do something.

· Directions should be clear and easy to understand.

Home Activity Your child is learning to write simple directions for how to do something. Share an activity at home and discuss how to do it.

1.19.A.1 Write brief compositions about topics of interest to the student.

Name _____

Circle the word for each picture.

1. zoo zip	2. span spoon	3. pal pool	4. stool stale
5. fruit fool	6. gaze goose	7. boot bait	8. spool spill

Pick a word to finish each sentence.

Write the word in the sentence.

9. The _____ blocked the cars on the road.

   moose   mouse

10. I dropped my _____ on the floor.

   farm   food

11. I used a _____ to clean up the mess.

   boot   broom

Home Activity Your child practiced reading and creating words with *oo* as in *moon*. Write the *oo* words from this page on scraps of paper. Have your child pick a word and use it in a sentence.

1.3.A.1.v.2. Decode words in context by applying common letter-sound correspondences, including: vowel digraphs including *oo* as in *moon*. Also 1.3.A.2.v.2.

Phonics Vowel Sound in *moon: oo*   493

Name _____

Words with Suffixes *-ly, -ful*

Spelling Words				
slowly	careful	quickly	useful	painful
playful	sadly	gladly	nicely	wonderful

Write the list word that means the same as the underlined words.

1. She said good-bye <u>in a sad way</u>.

1. _____

2. We had a <u>very good</u> time.

2. _____

3. Be <u>alert</u> when playing ball.

3. _____

4. The twins play <u>in a nice way</u>.

4. _____

5. Her foot was <u>full of pain</u>.

5. _____

6. I will <u>be happy to</u> help.

6. _____

7. The hamsters are <u>full of play</u>.

7. _____

8. Drive <u>in a slow way</u>.

8. _____

9. My pen is still <u>full of use</u>.

9. _____

10. He finished his work <u>in a fast way</u>.

10. _____

 Home Activity Your child spelled words with the suffixes *-ly* and *-ful*. Ask your child to explain what each suffix means. (Suffix *-ly* means "in a ___ way." Suffix *-ful* means "full of ___.")

1.22.A.1 Use phonological knowledge to match sounds to letters to construct words.

Name _____

Adjectives That Compare

Add **-er** to an adjective to compare
two persons, places, or things.

  The cat is **smaller** than the dog.

Add **-est** to an adjective to compare
three or more persons, places, or things.

  The mouse is **smallest** of the three.

Circle the adjectives that compare two things.
Underline the adjectives that compare three or more things.

  1. Mrs. Hopper is taller than Henry.

  2. Henry's father is tallest of the three.

  3. Mudge is smarter than that dog.

  4. Mudge is the smartest dog of all.

  5. Henry's mother is older than Henry.

  6. Mrs. Hopper is the oldest of the three.

Home Activity Your child learned about adjectives that compare. Read a story with your child. Have your
child look for adjectives that compare and tell what things are being compared.

1.20.A.3 Understand and use descriptive adjectives in the
context of reading, writing, and speaking.

Name _____

Sequence

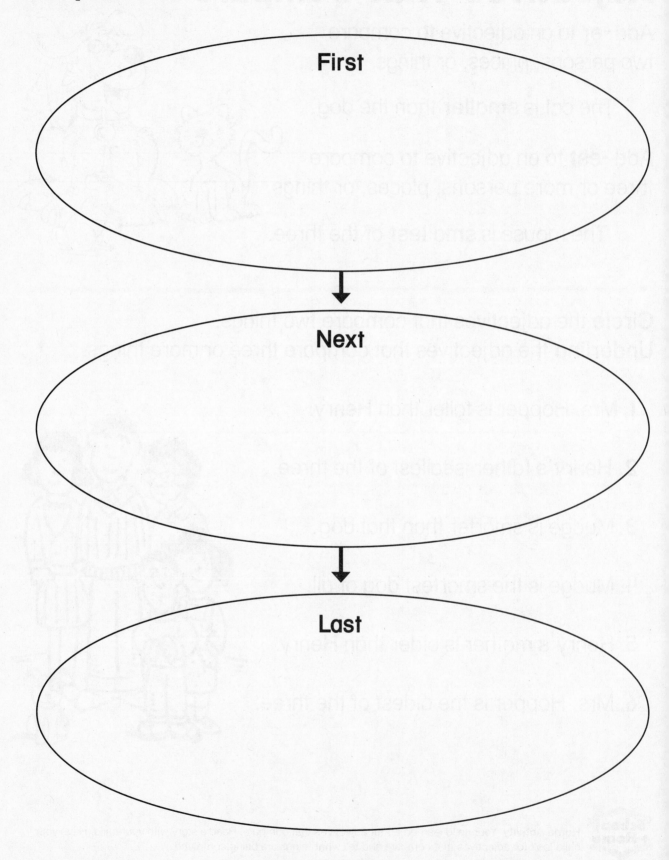

First

Next

Last

1.17.A Plan a first draft by generating ideas for writing.

Name _____

6   7   8   9   10

Trace and **write** the numbers.

6 _____

7 _____

8 _____

9 _____

10 _____

Circle your best number in each line.

Copy the sentence. Leave the correct space between words.

You can not be too helpful.

_____

Home Activity Your child practiced writing numbers 6, 7, 8, 9, 10 and sentences with words with *-ly*, *-ful*, and *oo*. Have your child practice writing the numbers one more time. Then write the following words on a sheet of paper and have your child read and rewrite them as neatly as possible: *skillful, softly, broom.*

1.21.A.1 Form upper-case letters legibly in text, using the basic conventions of print (left-to-right and top-to-bottom progression), including spacing between words and sentences. **Also 1.21.A.2.**

Handwriting   497

Name _____

Put each group of last names in ABC order.
Write the names on the lines.

Turza   Taylor   Terry   Till

1. _____

2. _____

3. _____

4. _____

Lin   Lewis   Lopez   Lance

5. _____

6. _____

7. _____

8. _____

Turn to the glossary on page 231 of your Unit 4 Student Edition.
What is the second word in ABC Order on the page?

9. _____

Home Activity Your child learned to use alphabetical order to find names in a phone book. The next time you need a phone number, ask your child to help you find the information.

1.24.B.1 Use text features in age-appropriate reference works to locate information.

Helping at a Zoo

Suffixes -ly, -ful	Vowel Sound in moon: oo		High-Frequency Words	
mainly	zoo	cool	a	some
quickly	bloom	soon	many	visit
likely	food	too	people	you
playful	broom			
painful	booth			

Many people help at a zoo.

Some mainly help flowers bloom.

Some get food for everyone.

You'll likely visit a zoo someday.

Will you go soon?

Will you help at a zoo too?

Decodable Story *Helping at a Zoo*
Target Skills Suffixes -ly, -ful; Vowel Sound in *moon: oo*

1.3.A.1.v.2 Decode words in context by applying common letter-sound correspondences, including: vowel digraphs including oo as in *moon*. **Also 1.3.H.2.**

Some helpers use a broom all day.

Some helpers sell treats in a booth.

Some helpers keep playful hippos cool.

A vet helps at a zoo.

A cub might get a painful cut.

A vet quickly helps its cut heal.

Name _____

Words with Suffixes -*ly*, -*ful*

Spelling Words	High-Frequency Words
slowly careful quickly useful painful	because
playful sadly gladly nicely wonderful	across

Write the suffix -*ly* or -*ful*. **Write** the word.

1. I went glad_____ .

2. The swimmers were care_____ .

3. It is a wonder_____ party.

4. A cell phone is very use_____ .

5. Mia plays nice_____ .

6. We quick_____ shut the door.

7. That's a play_____ kitten.

8. Cook the stew slow_____ .

Write the words to complete this sentence.

I went 9. _____ the street 10. _____ I saw my friend.

Home Activity Your child used spelling words to complete sentences. Read a sentence and have your child spell the list word.

1.22.A.1 Use phonological knowledge to match sounds to letters to construct words. 1.22.C.1 Spell high-frequency words from a commonly used list.

Spelling Words with Suffixes -*ly*, -*ful* **501**

Adjectives That Compare

Write about three special friends.
Use words from the box or your own
adjectives that compare.

| oldest   shorter   quieter   faster   tallest |

_____
- -
_____
- -
_____
- -
_____
- -
_____
- -
_____
- -
_____

School + Home

Home Activity Your child learned how to use adjectives that compare in writing. Talk about neighbors or family friends with your child. Together write sentences that compare two or more of these people. Use an adjective with *-er* or *-est* in each sentence.

502 **Conventions** Adjectives That Compare

1.20.A.3 Understand and use descriptive adjectives in the context of reading, writing, and speaking.

Name _____

Words with Suffixes *-ly, -ful*

Spelling Words				
slowly	careful	quickly	useful	painful
playful	sadly	gladly	nicely	wonderful

Circle the word that is spelled correctly.

1. sadly   sady

2. galadly   gladly

3. quickly   quikly

4. wondrful   wonderful

Write the list words in the puzzle.

Across

7. in a nice way

9. in a slow way

10. full of use

Down

5. full of pain

6. full of play

8. not careless

Home Activity Your child has been learning to spell words with the suffixes *-ly* and *-ful*. Say a base word. Ask your child to add *-ly* or *-ful* and say and spell the new word.

Adjectives That Compare

Mark the sentence that has a line under the adjective.

1. ○ Ms. Feld's lawn is <u>greener</u> than Mrs. Ho's lawn.
    ○ Ms. Feld's <u>lawn</u> is greener than Mrs. Ho's lawn.
    ○ Ms. Feld's lawn <u>is</u> greener than Mrs. Ho's lawn.

2. ○ <u>Mr. Jones</u> has the brownest lawn of all.
    ○ Mr. Jones <u>has</u> the brownest lawn of all.
    ○ Mr. Jones has the <u>brownest</u> lawn of all.

3. ○ Mr. Wyner's <u>trees</u> are shorter than Mrs. Garcia's trees.
    ○ Mr. Wyner's trees are <u>shorter</u> than Mrs. Garcia's trees.
    ○ Mr. Wyner's trees <u>are</u> shorter than Mrs. Garcia's trees.

4. ○ Mr. Scott has the tallest <u>trees</u> in the neighborhood.
    ○ Mr. Scott has the tallest trees in the <u>neighborhood</u>.
    ○ Mr. Scott has the <u>tallest</u> trees in the neighborhood.

5. ○ Our house is <u>older</u> than Mrs. Vin's house.
    ○ Our <u>house</u> is older than Mrs. Vin's house.
    ○ Our house is older <u>than</u> Mrs. Vin's house.

6. ○ <u>Dr. Ruiz</u> owns the newest house on our street.
    ○ Dr. Ruiz owns the <u>newest</u> house on our street.
    ○ Dr. Ruiz owns the newest house on our <u>street</u>.

School + Home **Home Activity** Your child prepared for taking tests on adjectives that compare. With your child, look through a newspaper or magazine article. Help your child circle adjectives that compare. Then discuss what each adjective is comparing.

⬇ 1.20.A.3 Understand and use descriptive adjectives in the context of reading, writing, and speaking.

Name _____

Pick a word from the box to match each picture.
Write it on the line.

cr**ow**n

┌───┐
│ cloud   clown   flower   house   │
└───┘

1.

_____
- - - - - - - - - - - - - - - -

2.

_____
- - - - - - - - - - - - - - - -

3.

_____
- - - - - - - - - - - - - - - -

4.

_____
- - - - - - - - - - - - - - - -

Unscramble the letters to make a word.

_____   _____   _____
- - - - - - - - -   - - - - - - - - -   - - - - - - - - -
uodl _____   wtno _____   tuo _____

Pick a word to finish each sentence. **Write** it on the line.

_____
- - - - - - - - -

5. The opposite of *in* is _____.

_____
- - - - - - - - -

6. The radio was too _____.

_____
- - - - - - - - -

7. I like to shop in _____.

School + Home

Home Activity Your child read and wrote words with *ow* that have the vowel sound heard in *crown*. Encourage your child to make a list of other words with *ow* that rhyme with *cow* and *brown*.

© Pearson Education, Inc., 1

1.3.A.1.vi.3 Decode words in context by applying common letter-sound correspondences, including: vowel diphthongs including *ou*.
Also 1.3.A.2.vi.3, 1.3.A.1.vi.4, 1.3.A.2.vi.4.

Phonics Diphthongs *ou, ow*   505

Name _____

Read the words in the box.
Pick a word to finish each sentence. **Write** it on the line.
Remember to use a capital letter at the beginning of a sentence.

| along | behind | eyes | never | pulling | toward |

---

1. The dogs walked _____ the wall.

2. The dogs stopped _____ the puddle.

---

3. Mom is _____ the boy away.

4. _____ pet a dog you do not know well.

---

5. The puppy ran _____ its mother.

6. Its _____ were happy and bright.

School + Home **Home Activity** Your child learned to identify and read the words *along, behind, eyes, never, pulling,* and *toward*. Ask your child to make up a puppet show using this week's words. Write out the script that your child dictates. Use paper bags or stick puppets to act it out.

1.3.H.1 Identify at least 100 high-frequency words from a commonly used list. **Also 1.3.H.2.**

Name _____

Read the story.
Write the answer to each question.

Many weeks ago, Tony and Dad planted daisy seeds. They planted the seeds in a sunny part of a garden. Soon daisy plants were growing in the garden. The plants grew very tall with many daisies. One night it rained hard. Tony went out to the garden the next day. He felt so sad. All the plants were bent down. Then Dad came with sticks and string. He tied the plants to the sticks. Soon the plants were standing up!

1. Who are the characters in the story?

_____
_____

2. Where does the story happen?

_____
_____

3. Why did Tony feel sad?

_____
_____

4. Why did Dad tie the plants to sticks?

_____
_____

5. How do you think Tony feels at the end of the story?

_____
_____

Home Activity Your child identified the characters, setting, and the problem and solution in a story. Together read a story that has an obvious problem and solution. Pause as you read to ask your child how the characters feel and why they feel that way.

Name _____

Writing • Animal Fantasy

 Cleaning Up

Bob and Sue were squirrels. They liked to play in the lot behind the hardware store. One day, a kid threw trash. Sue got angry.

Sue complained, "All this littering has to stop."

Bob said, "Yes. Let's get people to help clean."

Bob and Sue made signs for a cleanup on Saturday. They climbed trees and hung up the signs. On Saturday, many people showed up. No one knew who had the great idea to clean the lot. But everyone was glad to help. Now Bob and Sue have a great place to play!

Key Features of an Animal Fantasy

- characters are animals

- characters do things that real animals can't do

1.18.A Write brief stories that include a beginning, middle, and end.

Name _____

Circle the word for each picture.

 bott<u>le</u>

1.

cattle   canned

2.

tabbed   table

3.

picking   pickle

4.

turtle   turned

5.

candle   candy

6.

needy   needle

7.

handy   handle

8.

saddle   sadder

Find the word that has the same ending sound as .
Mark the ⬭ to show your answer.

9. ⬭ litter
⬭ lightly
⬭ little

10. ⬭ purple
⬭ purred
⬭ purest

School + Home

Home Activity Your child read two-syllable words with *-le* in the second syllable. Have your child fold a sheet of paper into four boxes, choose four of the words he or she circled, find a rhyming word for that word, and draw pictures of the rhyming word. Ask your child to label each picture.

1.3.C.1.iii Use common syllabication patterns to decode words, including: final stable syllable.

Phonics Final Syllable *-le*   509

Name _____

Words with *ow*

Spelling Words				
how	town	down	now	brown
cow	clown	frown	crowd	growl

Name the picture. **Write** a list word.

1. _____   2. _____   3. _____

Circle the correct word in the phrase. **Write** the word.

4. up and   **down**   **cow**

5. a   **brown**   **frown**   cow

6. **town**   **how**   about that

7. lost in the   **crowd**   **down**

8. the   **brown**   **growl**   of the lion

9. **clown**   **now**   and then

10. wipe off that   **frown**   **down**

4. _____

5. _____

6. _____

7. _____

8. _____

9. _____

10. _____

School + Home

Home Activity Your child spelled words with the vowel sound in *how*. Ask your child to name two letters common to all the spelling words. (*ow*)

⊕ **1.22.A.1** Use phonological knowledge to match sounds to letters to construct words.

Name _____

Imperative Sentences

An **imperative sentence** is a **command** sentence that tells someone to do something. It begins with a **capital letter.** It ends with a **period (.).**

Go to the garden**.**   Please watch the dog**.**

Underline each sentence that is a command.

1. Are you thirsty?

2. Pour a glass of milk.

3. You spilled some milk.

4. Please wipe up the milk.

5. Let me help you.

6. Drink your milk.

School + Home **Home Activity** Your child learned about commands. Explain how to play a game to your child. Have your child say "Command" each time he or she hears you use a command.

 1.1.D.1 Recognize distinguishing features of a sentence.
1.21.B.1.i Recognize basic capitalization for the beginning of sentences.

Name _____

Story Map

Characters

Setting

Events

Beginning

Middle

End

School + Home

Home Activity Your child is writing a story with animal characters. Together make up or remember a story about animal characters.

512 **Writing** Plan

🔖 **1.17.A** Plan a first draft by generating ideas for writing.

© Pearson Education, Inc., 1

Name _____

11 12 13 14 15

Trace and **write** the numbers.

11

12

13

14

15

Circle your best number in each line.

Copy the sentence. Leave the correct space between words.

The cow is in the stable.

_____

_____

Home Activity Your child practiced writing numbers 11, 12, 13, 14, 15 and sentences with words with *ou, ow,* and *-le.* Have your child practice writing the numbers one more time. Then have your child read and rewrite the sentence from above.

1.21.A.1 Form upper-case letters legibly in text, using the basic conventions of print (left-to-right and top-to-bottom progression), including spacing between words and sentences. **Also 1.21.A.2.**

Name _____

When does a problem have a clever solution?

> **Step 1—Think about problems that you have to solve.**

1. Write two or three problems.

   _____
   _____
   _____
   _____
   _____

> **Step 2—Choose a topic.**

2. Write the problem that you want to try to solve.

   _____
   _____

> **Step 3—Formulate research questions.**

3. Write two questions about the problem that you want to solve.

   _____
   _____
   _____
   _____

4. What sources of information could you use to help answer your questions about the problem?

   _____
   _____

Home Activity Your child learned how to generate topic ideas, formulate research questions, and choose reference sources. Talk to your child about problems around your home that need to be solved and help your child develop solutions.

1.23.A.1 Generate a list of topics of class-wide interest.
Also 1.23.A.2, 1.23.B.1.

Chow

Diphthongs ow and ou			Final Syllable -le	High-Frequency Words
Chow	town	ground	little	was
how	growl	around	beagle	a
bow	stout	grouch	tumble	said
now	hound	sound	Mingle	I
howl	proud	loud	puddle	the
scowled	found		nibble	to
			chuckle	is

Chow was a stout little beagle.

"See how my hound can tumble and bow?" said Miss Mingle. "I am proud!"

Then Miss Mingle got Chow a treat.

"Nibble this," she said with a chuckle.

"Now we'll all feel better!"

4

Decodable Story *Chow*
Target Skills Diphthongs *ow* and *ou*, Final Syllable *-le*

1.3.A.vi.3 Decode words in context and in isolation by applying common letter-sound correspondences, including: vowel diphthongs including *ou*. **Also 1.3.A.1.vi.4, 1.3.A.2.vi.4, 1.3.C.iii, 1.3.H.2.**

Chow found a puddle on the ground.

He splashed mud all around.

"Now I am a grouch!" said Miss Mingle.

Chow started to howl.

"That sound is too loud," Miss Mingle scowled.

"Everyone in town will growl!"

Name _____

Words with *ow*

Spelling Words				
how	town	down	now	brown
cow	clown	frown	crowd	growl

High-Frequency Words
eyes
never

Write the missing list word.

1. We saw him milk a _____ .

2. Don't get lost in the _____ .

3. Her hair is _____ .

4. Do you know _____ to skate?

5. I heard the dog _____ .

6. We have a park in our _____ .

7. Let's go _____ the slide.

8. The best time is _____ .

9. I closed my _____ .

10. I will _____ stop laughing.

Home Activity Your child wrote spelling words to complete sentences. Have your child spell a list word and use it in a sentence.

⊛ **1.22.A.1** Use phonological knowledge to match sounds to letters to construct words. **1.22.C.1** Spell high-frequency words from a commonly used list.

Name _____

Imperative Sentences

Pam has a problem with her cat.
What should Pam do?
Tell what Pam should do.
Write about your ideas.
Use commands.

_____
- -
_____
- -
_____
- -
_____
- -
_____
- -
_____
- -
_____
- -

Home Activity Your child learned how to use commands in writing. Ask your child to write about how to make a sandwich. Then have your child underline commands he or she used.

1.1.D.1 Recognize distinguishing features of a sentence.
1.21.B.1.i Recognize basic capitalization for the beginning of sentences.

Name _____

Words with *ow*

Spelling Words				
how	town	down	now	brown
cow	clown	frown	crowd	growl

Unscramble the letters. **Write** the list word.

1. **l o c n w**

1. _____

2. **w o h**

2. _____

3. **b n r o w**

3. _____

4. **w l g r o**

4. _____

5. **o w c**

5. _____

6. **n t w o**

6. _____

7. **o n w**

7. _____

Write the missing words.

8. The _____ had to wait in a long line.

9. There was no place to sit _____ .

10. Everyone began to _____ .

Home Activity Your child has been learning to spell words with the vowel sound in *how*. Give clues about a word. Ask your child to guess and spell the word.

1.22.A.1 Use phonological knowledge to match sounds to letters to construct words.

Spelling Words with *ow* 519

Imperative Sentences

Mark the sentence that has a command.

1. ○ Look in the newspaper.
   ○ Will you look in the newspaper?
   ○ Ben looks in the newspaper.

2. ○ Meg will find the answer.
   ○ Find the answer.
   ○ Did she find the answer?

3. ○ Cam left the key here.
   ○ Where is the key?
   ○ Please find the key.

4. ○ Will the glue hold the pieces together?
   ○ I will glue the pieces together.
   ○ Glue the pieces together.

5. ○ Who dropped the letter in the box?
   ○ Please drop the letter in the box.
   ○ Ann dropped the letter in the box.

6. ○ Look at this dirty shirt.
   ○ This shirt is dirty.
   ○ Why is this shirt dirty?

Home Activity Your child prepared for taking tests on commands. Together read a favorite story. Have your child point out commands, questions, and statements in the story.

1.1.D.1 Recognize distinguishing features of a sentence.
1.21.B.1.i Recognize basic capitalization for the beginning of sentences.

Name _____

Write a word from the box
to match each picture.

couch	cow	flour
snowman	towel	rowboat

1. [couch illustration]
_____
- - - - - - - - - - - -
_____

2. [rowboat illustration]
_____
- - - - - - - - - - - -
_____

3.
_____
- - - - - - - - - - - -
_____

4.
_____
- - - - - - - - - - - -
_____

5. [snowman illustration]
_____
- - - - - - - - - - - -
_____

6.
_____
- - - - - - - - - - - -
_____

Write the word to finish each sentence. **Remember** to use capital
letters at the beginning of a sentence.

_____
- - - - - - - - - - - - - - - - - - - -
7. _____ does your garden grow? **how   have**

- - - - - - - - - - - - - - - - -
8. Can I come to play at your _____? **toy   house**

- - - - - - - - - - - - - -
9. I like to _____ bubbles. **blue   blow**

- - - - - - - - - - - - - -
10. I went _____ to take a walk. **outside   inside**

School + Home

Home Activity Your child read and wrote words with vowel patterns *ou* as in *couch*, and *ow* as in *cow* and
snow. Encourage your child to make a list of words that rhyme with these vowel patterns.

1.3.A.2.v.6 Decode words in isolation by applying common letter-
sound correspondences, including: vowel digraphs including *ow* as in
how. **Also 1.3.A.1.v.6, 1.3.A.1.v.8, 1.3.A.2.v.8, A.3.A.1.v.7, 1.3.A.2.v.7.**

Name _____

Read the words in the box.
Pick a word to finish each sentence.
Write it on the line.

(door   loved   should   wood)

Dear Jack,

I had such a good time at your house last week.
_____

I _____ it when we played in the snow!
Remember when we made an igloo?
_____

We used a blanket for the _____, and it froze stiff.
_____

You _____ come to my house!
It is very warm here even in the winter.
_____

My dad and I are going to paint the _____ rail.

Your friend,

Sam

Home Activity Your child learned to identify and read the words *door, loved, should,* and *wood*. Ask your child to write a story that uses each word and read it aloud.

1.3.H.1 Identify at least 100 high-frequency words from a commonly used list. **Also 1.3.H.2.**

Name _____

Read the story.
Write an answer to each question.

Jean painted a picture of a vase with roses in it. Some of the roses were red. Some were yellow roses. The vase was blue. Jean took her picture to an art show. A man hung Jean's picture on a wall. Many people came to the show to see the pictures. Then Jean saw a blue tag on her picture. The man handed Jean the blue tag. All the people clapped.

1. Why do you think the people clapped?

_____

_____

_____

_____

_____

2. What do you think the blue tag means?

_____

_____

_____

_____

_____

3. What do you think Jean will do next?

_____

_____

_____

_____

_____

Home Activity Your child used what he or she already knew about a situation to draw conclusions about an event. Reread the story with your child. Have your child tell you what he or she already knew about art shows that helped him or her draw conclusions about the story.

1.9 Draw conclusions about the structure and elements of fiction.

Comprehension Draw Conclusions **523**

Writing · Letter to a Character

Dear Mr. Wolf,

I have read a lot of books where you always seem to show up and cause trouble. It makes me angry to see you blow the pigs' houses down. What did they ever do to you?

It makes me sad to see you scare Little Red Riding Hood. She is just trying to get through the woods to see her grandma.

So, please Mr. Wolf, try to be nice and stop scaring people and ruining their homes.

Thank you,
Patrick

Key Features of a Letter to a Character

· describes feelings or opinions to a story character

· includes a friendly greeting and closing

1.19.B Write short letters that put ideas in a chronological or logical sequence and use appropriate conventions (e.g., date, salutation, closing). **1.19.C.1** Write brief comments about literary texts.

Name _____

Circle the word for each picture.

 <u>sofa</u>

1.	2.	3.	4.
lesson lemon	pillow pilot	bacon basket	wagging wagon

5.	6.	7.	8.
river rigged	cabin cab	timber tiger	came camel

Draw a picture for each word.

9. spider

10. baby

Home Activity Your child read words with two syllables that have one consonant in the middle. Have your child choose five words from the page and use each word in a sentence.

1.3.C.1.i Use common syllabication patterns to decode words, including: closed syllable (CVC). **Also 1.3.C.1.ii.**

Name _____

Words with *ou*

Read the clue. **Write** the list word.

It starts with **h**, and it rhymes with **mouse**.

1. _____

It starts with **cl**, and it rhymes with **loud**.

2. _____

It starts with **sh**, and it rhymes with **pout**.

3. _____

It starts with **o**, and it rhymes with **couch**.

4. _____

Spelling Words

mouth

house

found

our

out

cloud

ouch

shout

round

count

Write the missing list word.

5. Look at _____ pups.

6. We _____ them last week.

7. Can you _____ them?

8. One pup wants to get _____ .

9. He put a ball in his _____ .

10. The ball is _____ .

Home Activity Your child spelled words with the vowel sound in *out*. Ask your child to name two letters common to all the spelling words. (*ou*)

526 **Spelling** Words with *ou*

🌐 **1.22.A.1** Use phonological knowledge to match sounds to letters to construct words.

Pronouns

A **pronoun** is a word that takes the place of a noun or nouns. The words **he, she, it, we, you,** and **they** are pronouns.

People see the bird.   **They** see the bird.

Jake helps the bird.   **He** helps the bird.

Circle the pronoun in each sentence.
Say a sentence for each pronoun.

1. We need to feed the birds.

2. They like to eat.

3. He likes the wild bird.

4. It can fly away.

Circle the pronoun in ( ) that takes the place of the underlined word or words.

5. <u>This bird</u> is little. (She, It)

6. <u>Mole and I</u> went to the forest. (He, We)

7. <u>Mole</u> gets food for the bird. (He, They)

8. <u>Mole and Grandad</u> let the bird go. (They, You)

 Home Activity Your child learned about pronouns. Write *he, she, it, we, you,* and *they* in a list. Point to each word and ask your child to use it in a sentence.

1.20.A.6 Understand and use pronouns in the context of reading, writing, and speaking.

Name _____

Letter Format

Dear _____ ,

_____

- -

_____

- -

_____

- -

_____

- -

_____

- -

_____

- -

_____

- -

_____

- -

_____

- -

_____ ,

- -

_____

School + Home

Home Activity Your child can express opinions about a story. Discuss a book you both have liked.

🟊 **1.17.A** Plan a first draft by generating ideas for writing.

Name _____

16 17 18 19 20

Trace and **write** the numbers.

16 _____

17 _____

18 _____

19 _____

20 _____

Copy the sentence. Leave the correct space between words.

The baby camel is cute.

_____

_____

Did you leave the correct space between your words? | Yes | | No |

Home Activity Your child practiced writing numbers *16, 17, 18, 19, 20* and words with short and long vowels. Have your child practice writing the numbers one more time. Then have your child read and rewrite the sentence from above.

Name _____

Read the numbered words in each list.
Match each numbered word with the guide words that show where you would find the word in a dictionary.
Draw a line from the numbered word to its guide words.

1. mouth   A. part / plant

2. picture   B. gerbil / goose

3. give   C. mouse / much

4. dance   D. damp / date

5. because   E. clam / cube

6. color   F. bark / beep

7. present   G. name / nice

8. draw   H. dish / duck

9. never   I. porch / price

Home Activity Your child learned about using alphabetical order and guide words in a dictionary. Help your child look up other words in a dictionary at home.

🌐 **1.23.B.1** Decide what sources of information might be relevant to answer these questions. **Also 1.24.B.1.**

A New Home

Vowel Patterns *ow* (how)(show), *ou*		Syllables V/CV and VC/V		High-Frequency Words	
brown	windows	found	Toby's	city	a	is
now	throw	house	tiny	models	I	of
down	yellow	out	begin	comics	the	to
town	pillow		baby	closet	said	their
			label			

Toby's dad got a new job.

"I found a brown house in the city," he said.

"It is tiny, but it has lots of windows."

1

Dad and Toby missed their house in town.

But Dad liked his new job, and Toby liked his shiny new closet!

4

Decodable Story *A New Home*
Target Skills Vowel Patterns *ow* (how, show), *ou*; Syllables V/CV and VC/V

1.3.A.2.v.7 Decode words in isolation by applying common letter-sound correspondences, including: vowel digraphs including *ow* as in *snow*. **Also** 1.3.A.1.v.6, 1.3.A.2.v.6, 1.3.A.1.v.7, 1.3.A.1.v.8, 1.3.A.2.v.8, 1.3.A.1.vi.3, 1.3.A.1.vi.4, 1.3.D.1.

"I'll begin to pack right now,"
said Toby.

"I'll throw out my yellow baby
pillow,

but I'll pack my models and
comics!"

"I'll label the boxes," said Dad.

"We'll take them down to the
truck."

Name _____

Words with *ou*

Spelling Words				
mouth	house	found	our	out
cloud	ouch	shout	round	count

High-Frequency Words
loved
should

Read about finding bugs. **Write** the missing list words.

1. We _____ some bugs.

2. They are _____ .

3. Let's _____ them.

4. One got in my _____ .

5. Did you _____ ?

6. I said _____ .

7. I spit it _____ .

8. Look at that _____ !

9. The bugs _____ not be here.

10. No one _____ these bugs.

Home Activity Your child used spelling words and high-frequency words to complete sentences. Read a sentence on this page. Have your child spell the list word.

1.22.A.1 Use phonological knowledge to match sounds to letters to construct words. **1.22.C.1** Spell high-frequency words from a commonly used list.

Name _____

Pronouns

Look at the picture.
Write about what the people are doing.
Use pronouns.

_____
- -
_____
- -
_____
- -
_____
- -
_____

Find other pronouns. **Say** a sentence for each pronoun.

Home Activity Your child learned how to use pronouns in writing. With your child, look through a family photo album. Talk about what you see in the photos, using pronouns instead of names.

534 Conventions Pronouns

⊕ **1.20.A.6** Understand and use pronouns in the context of reading, writing, and speaking.

Name _____

Words with *ou*

Spelling Words				
mouth	house	found	our	out
cloud	ouch	shout	round	count

Write the words in the puzzle.

1. | | o | u | | |

2. | o | u | | |

3. | o | u | |

4. | | | o | u | |

cloud
ouch
out
mouth

Connect the matching list words.

5. found

6. round

7. our

9. shout

found

8. house

house

10. count

count

shout

round

our

School + Home

Home Activity Your child has been learning to spell words with the vowel sound in *out*. Draw a big butterfly. Have your child write the list words on the wings.

1.22.A.1 Use phonological knowledge to match sounds to letters to construct words.

Spelling Words with *ou* 535

Pronouns

Mark the pronoun that can replace each underlined word or words.

1. <u>Birds</u> can fly.
   - ○ **A** He
   - ○ **B** It
   - ○ **C** They

2. <u>A mole</u> is an animal.
   - ○ **A** It
   - ○ **B** She
   - ○ **C** You

3. <u>Mole and I</u> feed the bird.
   - ○ **A** It
   - ○ **B** We
   - ○ **C** She

4. <u>Ann</u> plays with the bird.
   - ○ **A** She
   - ○ **B** They
   - ○ **C** We

5. <u>Rob</u> makes a nest.
   - ○ **A** They
   - ○ **B** He
   - ○ **C** It

Say a sentence for each pronoun.

Home Activity Your child prepared for taking tests on pronouns. Together look through a newspaper or magazine article. Take turns finding and circling the pronouns *he, she, it, we, you,* and *they.*

✦ **1.20.A.6** Understand and use pronouns in the context of reading, writing, and speaking.

Name _____

Circle the word for each picture.

1.	2.	3.	4.
had hood	cook coat	hook hard	wide wood

5.	6.	7.	8.
bake book	look lock	store stood	brook brake

Read the words in the box.
Circle the words that have the same vowel sound as .
Pick one of these words to finish each sentence.

> take   foot   took   soon   goat   tool   good

_____

9. He _____ a picture of the lake.

10. That was a _____ joke.

11. My _____ hurts.

School + Home

Home Activity Your child read and wrote words with *oo* that have the vowel sound heard in *foot*. Encourage your child to make lists that sort the words into those that rhyme with *took* and those that rhyme with *good*.

1.3.A.1.v.1 Decode words in context by applying common letter-sound correspondences, including: vowel digraphs including *oo* as in *foot*. Also 1.3.A.2.v.1.

Phonics Vowel Sound in *foot: oo*   537

Name _____

Dot & Jabber

Read the sentence. **Unscramble** the letters.
Write the word on the line. **Remember** to use
a capital letter at the beginning of a sentence.

among   another   instead   none

1. I will have **ahernot**.
_____
- - - - - - - - - - - - - - - - - -
_____

2. **eNon** of the fruit is left.
_____
- - - - - - - - - - - - - - - - - -
_____

3. Eat this **ineadst**.
_____
- - - - - - - - - - - - - - - - - -
_____

4. He likes to nap **angmo** his dogs.
_____
- - - - - - - - - - - - - - - - - -
_____

Home Activity Your child learned to identify and read the words *among, another, instead,* and *none*. Write sentences such as these: *Is there another towel like this one? Try this one instead. None of the pie is left.* Leave a blank where the word should be, and have your child fill it in.

538 **High-Frequency Words**

1.3.H.1 Identify at least 100 high-frequency words from a commonly used list. **Also 1.3.H.2.**

Name _____

Read the story. **Look** at the pictures.

Circle the answer to each question.

Chick and Spot are friends. They do not fight. They like to play games. Sometimes, they chase each other around the yard. I laugh when I watch them play.

1. Who is big?   Spot   Chick

_____

2. Who is small?   Spot   Chick

_____

3. Who can bark?   Spot   Chick

_____

4. Who is standing?   Spot   Chick

_____

5. Who has wings?   Spot   Chick

_____

6. **Draw** two cats that look the same.

7. **Draw** two cats that do not look the same.

School + Home

Home Activity Your child compared and contrasted characters in a story. As you read stories with your child, have him or her compare the characters in the stories.

RC-1.D.1 Make inferences about text. **Also** RC-1.D.2.

Comprehension Compare and Contrast   **539**

Name _____

Writing · Questions

 Animals in Africa

What animals can I see in Africa?

When do giraffes sleep?

How much does an elephant weigh?

A male elephant weighs about 12,000 pounds. A female elephant weighs about 7,000 pounds.

Key Features of Questions

• Many *start* with the words **who, what, where, when,** or **how.**

• Questions end with a question mark.

1.19.A.1 Write brief compositions about topics of interest to the student.

Name _____

Add -s, -ed, or **-ing** to the word in ( ).
Write the new word on the line.

(hope + -s)

_____

- - - - - - - - - - - - - - - - - -

1. Jean _____ to grow corn.

(slope + -ing)

_____

- - - - - - - - - - - - - - - - - - -

2. She plants seeds on the _____ hill.

(care + -ed)

_____

- - - - - - - - - - - - - - - - - -

3. Jean _____ for the plants.

(taste + -ed)

_____

- - - - - - - - - - - - - - - - -

4. Jean _____ the corn.

(smile + -ing)

_____

- - - - - - - - - - - - - - - - -

5. She is _____ .

Home Activity Your child added *-s*, *-ed*, or *-ing* to verbs that end in *e*. Write *hope, slope, care, taste,* and *smile* on a sheet of paper. Ask your child to tell the rule about adding *-s*, *-ed*, or *-ing* to each word. Then write the new words.

© Pearson Education, Inc., 1

Words with *oo*

Circle the words in the box that rhyme. **Write** them.

foot	took
look	pool

1. _____
2. _____

foot	moon
book	noon

3. _____
4. _____

Spelling Words

- book
- moon
- took
- food
- look
- pool
- zoo
- noon
- good
- foot

Write a word that often goes with the list word.

5. bad   5. _____

6. hand   6. _____

7. drink   7. _____

Write the missing list word.

8. Greg wants to read a _____ .

9. Ann wants to swim at the _____ .

10. Joe wants to feed deer at the _____ .

School + Home

Home Activity Your child spelled words with the vowel sounds in *book* and *moon*. Ask your child to pronounce each list word and identify the vowel sound.

1.22.A.1 Use phonological knowledge to match sounds to letters to construct words.

Pronouns *I* and *Me*

The pronouns I and **me** take the place of your name. Use I in the subject of a sentence. Use **me** after an action verb. Always write I with a capital letter.

Dot calls **me**. I talk to her.

When you talk about yourself and another person, name yourself last.

Jabber and I talk on the phone. Dot calls Jabber and **me**.

Write **I** or **me** to complete each sentence.

1. _____ see an acorn.

2. It gives _____ an idea.

3. _____ take the acorn home.

4. Dot and _____ paint it.

5. See Dot and _____ hide the acorn.

Home Activity Your child learned about using *I* and *me*. Take turns telling about ways you use the telephone. Use *I* and *me* as you talk.

1.20.A.6 Understand and use pronouns in the context of reading, writing, and speaking. **Also 1.21.B.1.ii, 1.21.B.2.ii.**

Name _____

Topics for Questions

Questions

1. _____

2. _____

3. _____

1.17.A Plan a first draft by generating ideas for writing.

Name _____

Copy the **sentences**. Leave the correct space between words.

1. We hoped mom baked.

----

2. I am taking this book.

----

3. They smiled at us.

----

4. He is judging a contest.

----

5. We liked making juice.

Did you leave the correct space between your words? | Yes | | No |

Home Activity Your child practiced writing sentences with words with added endings such as *-ed* and *-ing*. Write these words on a sheet of paper: *hide, ride, shine*. Have your child copy each word and then drop the *e* and add *-ing* to write the new word.

1.21.A.1 Form upper-case letters legibly in text, using the basic conventions of print (left-to-right and top-to-bottom progression), including spacing between words and sentences. **Also 1.21.A.2.**

Name _____

Read the article. **Write** the answers.

Acorns

Acorns are <u>nuts</u>. They are the fruit of the
oak tree. They fall to the ground in the FALL.

Who Eats Acorns
- Squirrels
- Mice
- Birds

The squirrel often buries his acorns.
He eats them in the WINTER.

1. What is the title of the article? _____

2. Use the picture to write a sentence about squirrels.

_____

_____

_____

3. Write a heading from the article. _____

_____

_____

4. Which words are all capitals? _____

Home Activity Your child learned about text features. Look through nonfiction books with your child. Have
your child point out text features, such as titles, subheads, and words that are all capitals or are in italics or
boldface.

1.24.B.1 Use text features in age-appropriate reference works to
locate information.

Going for a Drive

Vowel Sound in *foot: oo*	Drop Final *e* to Add Endings		High-Frequency Words	
stood	smiling	saving	was	what
good	driving	piling	a	to
shook	taking	riding	said	I
cookies	baking	waving	their	go
cookbook	writing		the	
look				

Dad was smiling. He stood up.

"It's a good day for driving," he said.

"I'm taking everyone with me. Let's go!"

1

"We're piling in the car and riding downtown," said Dad, waving at the kids.

"I know just the place to go!"

4

Decodable Story *Going for a Drive*
Target Skills Vowel Sound in *foot: oo*; Drop Final *e* to Add Endings

1.3.A.1.v.1 Decode words in context by applying common letter-sound correspondences, including: vowel digraphs including *oo* as in *foot*. **Also** 1.3.A.2.v.1, 1.3.E.1.

Lacy and Mike shook their heads.

"We're baking cookies, but we can't find the cookbook."

Jon and Margo shook their heads.

"We're writing about saving the whales, but we don't know what to look up."

Name _____

Words with *oo*

Spelling Words					High-Frequency Words
book	moon	took	food	look	instead
pool	zoo	noon	good	foot	another

Choose a word to finish the sentence.
Fill in the circle. **Write** the word.

1. I ○ **took** ○ **look** ○ **foot** a sack lunch.

2. Read the ○ **took** ○ **zoo** ○ **book**.

3. My ○ **foot** ○ **noon** ○ **took** got wet.

4. We need more ○ **noon** ○ **food** ○ **look**.

5. Bears are at the ○ **zoo** ○ **moon** ○ **foot**.

6. That is ○ **look** ○ **good** ○ **took** news.

7. We swim in the ○ **noon** ○ **foot** ○ **pool**.

8. The ○ **look** ○ **took** ○ **moon** is bright.

Write the word that matches each clue.

9. in- _____

10. an- _____

Home Activity Your child wrote spelling words and high-frequency words to complete sentences. Have your child create a sentence using three or more list words.

1.22.A.1 Use phonological knowledge to match sounds to letters to construct words. 1.22.C.1 Spell high-frequency words from a commonly used list.

Spelling Words with *oo* **549**

Pronouns *I* and *Me*

Answer the question.
Change the words to write the answer.

Can I solve the mystery?

_____
- -
_____

Write sentences about a mystery you solved.
Use I and **me.**

_____
- -
_____
- -
_____
- -
_____
- -
_____
- -
_____

Home Activity Your child learned how to use *I* and *me* in writing. Have your child read aloud the sentences he or she wrote on this page. Ask your child to point out the *I*'s and *me*'s.

★ **1.20.A.6** Understand and use pronouns in the context of reading, writing, and speaking. **1.20.C.1** Ask questions with appropriate subject-verb inversion.

Words with oo

Write the missing letters.

1. ____ **oo** ____   2. ____ **oo** ____

3. ____ **oo** ____   4. ____ **oo** ____

Spelling Words

book

moon

took

food

look

pool

zoo

noon

good

foot

Write the list words in the puzzle.

Across

6. 12:00
8. you eat this
10. see

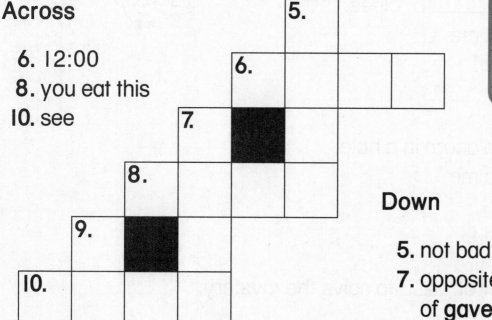

Down

5. not bad
7. opposite of **gave**
9. animals live there

School + Home

Home Activity Your child has been learning to spell words with the vowel sounds in *book* and *moon*. Write *oo* and pronounce a list word. Have your child add letters to spell the word. Continue with other list words.

1.22.A.1 Use phonological knowledge to match sounds to letters to construct words.

Spelling Words with *oo*   551

Pronouns *I* and *Me*

Mark the letter of the word or words that complete each sentence.

1. _____ saw a squirrel.
   - ○ Dad and me
   - ○ Dad and I
   - ○ Me

2. _____ found an acorn.
   - ○ Me
   - ○ Dad and me
   - ○ I

3. Jabber asks _____ for clues.
   - ○ Dot and me
   - ○ Dot and I
   - ○ I

4. _____ put the acorn in a hole.
   - ○ Dot and me
   - ○ Me
   - ○ Dot and I

5. It was clever of _____ to solve the mystery.
   - ○ I
   - ○ me
   - ○ me and I

Home Activity Your child prepared for taking tests on using *I* and *me*. Ask your child to read the sentences on this page and to say the word or words that complete each sentence as he or she reads it.

1.20.A.6 Understand and use pronouns in the context of reading, writing, and speaking.

Circle the word for each picture.

 t<u>oy</u>   s<u>oi</u>l

1.	2.	3.	4.
coins canes	bay boy	boil bail	joy jay

5.	6.	7.	8.
boil book	all oil	foil fail	round royal

Pick a word to finish each sentence. **Write** the word in the sentence.

9. May I _____ you for lunch?   (jolly, join)

10. My favorite _____ is a racing car.   (tray, toy)

11. The meat will _____ in the hot sun.   (spoil, spool)

 School + Home   **Home Activity** Your child read and wrote words with *oi* and *oy* as heard in *toy* and *soil*. Have your child sort the *oi* and *oy* words on this page and make two lists. Then have him or her read the words aloud.

1.3.A.1.vi.1 Decode words in context by applying common letter-sound correspondences, including: vowel diphthongs including *oy*. **Also** 1.3.A.2.vi.1, 1.3.A.1.vi.2, 1.3.A.2.vi.2.

Phonics Diphthongs *oi, oy*   **553**

Name _____

Read the words in the box.
Pick a word to finish each sentence.
Write it in the puzzle.

against   goes   heavy   kinds   today

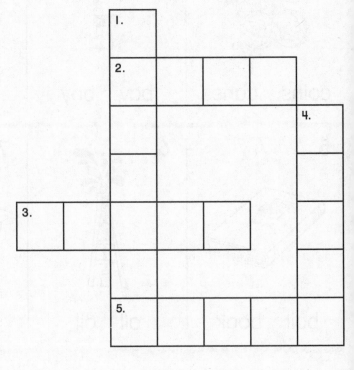

I. We push the
   umbrella _____ the wind.

2. The rain _____ into
   our shoes.

3. We play all _____ of
   games in the big puddles!

4. Rain this _____ does
   not happen often.

5. We will need
   dry socks _____ !

Home Activity Your child learned to read the words *against, goes, heavy, kinds,* and *today.* Ask your child
to use the words in a silly song. Write the words of the song and invite him or her to illustrate it.

1.3.H.1 Identify at least 100 high-frequency words from a
commonly used list. **Also 1.3.H.2.**

Name _____

Read the story.
Circle the sentence that tells what the story is all about.
Draw a picture of what the story is about.

1. The ground felt soft under my feet. The trees were tall and green. The air was warm. I liked hiking in the forest.

2.

Read the title of the story.
Circle a detail that might be in the story.
Draw a picture of that detail.

3. Title: The Party
Jen and Fran sang "Happy Birthday."
Jen and Fran have bikes.
Jen and Fran like school.

4.

Home Activity Your child learned about the main idea and details of a story. As you read stories with your child, have your child tell you what the story is all about. Have your child tell you details from the story.

1.13.A.1 Identify the topic. **Also 1.14.A.1, 1.14.B.1, 1.14.B.2.**

Comprehension Main Idea and Details **555**

Name _____

Writing · Advertisement

 You Need a Computer!

Everyone needs a computer!

A computer can help you find information.

You can find facts about your favorite animal.

A computer can help you stay in touch.

You can use it to send an e-mail to a friend.

You can use a computer to buy things.

You can even use it to watch a movie.

Buy a computer today!

Key Features of an Advertisement

· An advertisement promotes a product or a service.

· An advertisement describes the product or service.

1.19.A.1 Write brief compositions about topics of interest to the student.

Name _____

Write a word from the box
to match each picture.

work**er**

| baker sailor painter teacher |

1.

_____
- - - - - - - - - - - - - - - -
_____

2.

_____
- - - - - - - - - - - - - - - -
_____

3.

_____
- - - - - - - - - - - - - - - -
_____

4.

_____
- - - - - - - - - - - - - - - -
_____

Draw a picture of each word.

5. driver

6. actor

School + Home

Home Activity Your child read and wrote words that end in -er and -or as in worker and actor. Write each word on a slip of paper. Have your child choose a slip and act out the word for you to guess.

1.3.C Use common syllabication patterns to decode words.
Also 1.3.D.

Phonics Suffixes -er, -or **557**

Name _____

Words with *oi, oy*

Spelling Words				
oil	soil	voice	point	boy
boil	coin	oink	toy	join

Circle the rhyming words in each row. **Write** them.

toy   oil   boil   1. _____   2. _____

coin   join   boil   3. _____   4. _____

toy   soil   boy   5. _____   6. _____

Read the sentence. **Write** a list word that means the same as the underlined word.

7. Do you hear the big pig <u>squeal</u>?   7. _____

8. The farmer's <u>sound</u> is loud.   8. _____

9. The post has a sharp <u>end</u>.   9. _____

10. The <u>ground</u> is very muddy.   10. _____

Home Activity Your child spelled words with the vowel sound in *boy* spelled *oi* and *oy*. Ask your child to pronounce each list word, spell it, and then check the spelling.

🟢 **1.22.A.1** Use phonological knowledge to match sounds to letters to construct words.

More About Pronouns

A **pronoun** can take the place of some words in a sentence. **I, you, he, she, it, we,** and **they** are used in the **naming part** of a sentence. **Me, you, him, her, it, us,** and **them** are used in the **action part** of a sentence.

Ben likes **machines**. **He** makes **them**.

Write the pronoun in ( ) that can take the place of the underlined word or words.

1. Sara uses a lever. (Him, She)

2. Pulleys are all around. (They, Them)

3. Ben helps Sara. (He, Him)

4. Sara sees the machines. (She, Her)

5. Sara likes the machines. (them, they)

6. I like Ben's machine. (her, it)

Home Activity Your child learned more about pronouns. Ask your child to make up new sentences using the pronouns he or she wrote on this page.

1.20.A.6 Understand and use pronouns in the context of reading, writing, and speaking.

Name _____

Web B

Home Activity Your child can write about topics such as machines. Discuss machines in your home and good ways to use them.

🟉 **1.17.A** Plan a first draft by generating ideas for writing.

Name _____

Copy the **sentences.** Leave the correct space between words.

1. The boy is noisy.

2. We lost the coin.

3. I did enjoy it.

4. Roy is a good baker.

5. My dad is a sailor.

Did you leave the correct space between your words? | Yes | | No |

Home Activity Your child practiced writing sentences with words with *oy, oi, er,* and *or.* Write these words on a sheet of paper: *boil, corn, Mother, will, the.* Have your child rewrite the words to make a sentence. *(Mother will boil the corn.)*

1.21.A.1 Form upper-case letters legibly in text, using the basic conventions of print (left-to-right and top-to-bottom progression), including spacing between words and sentences. **Also 1.21.A.2.**

Handwriting   561

Name _____

Amy asked her friends which invention they liked the most.
Help Amy complete the picture graph.

Favorite Inventions

Number of Children

8
7
6
5
4
3
2
1
0

Car   Television   Telephone   Computer

1. Eight friends like cars the most. **Draw** eight cars on the picture graph.

2. Seven friends like television the most. **Draw** seven televisions on the picture graph.

3. Three friends like telephones the most. **Draw** three telephones on the picture graph.

4. Five friends like computers the most. **Draw** five computers on the picture graph.

5. Present Amy's results to your class by acting out the creation of the invention that her classmates liked most.

School + Home **Home Activity** Your child learned to make a picture graph. Together, make a picture graph that shows information about your family, such as favorite foods or favorite hobbies of each family member.

1.26.A.1 Create a visual display (with adult assistance) to convey the results of the research. **Also 1.24.C.1.**

What Are You?

Diphthongs oi, oy	Suffixes -er, -or		High-Frequency Words
soil	reader	singer	a
coins	writer	actor	are
boy	talker	baker	you
toy	dreamer	maker	do
joy	runner	farmer	the
	skater	banker	many

You're a boy or girl.

You're a reader and writer.

You're a talker and dreamer.

You are good at many things.

Try new things.

Keep doing the things that bring you joy!

Decodable Story *What Are You?*
Target Skills Diphthongs *oi, oy;* Suffixes *-er, -or*

1.3.A.1.vi.1 Decode words in context by applying common letter-sound correspondences, including: vowel diphthongs including *oy*. **Also 1.3.A.1.vi.2.**

Are you a fast runner or skater?

Are you a good singer or actor?

Are you a baker or toy maker?

Do you like the soil?

Do you collect coins?

Will you be a farmer or a banker?

Name _____

Words with *oi, oy*

Spelling Words				
oil	soil	voice	point	boy
boil	coin	oink	toy	join

High-Frequency Words
heavy
against

Circle a word to finish the sentence. **Write** the word.

1. Cover the seeds with **soil toy**.

_____

2. He put a **voice coin** in his bank.

_____

3. I will **boil point** to the answer.

_____

4. Is this wagon your **soil toy**?

_____

5. The pigs began to **oink coin**.

_____

6. Did you **voice join** the club?

_____

7. I saw a **boy oil** in the hall.

_____

8. She spoke in a soft **coin voice**.

_____

9. Put the bike **against heavy** the wall.

_____

10. The rock was so **against heavy**.

_____

Home Activity Your child wrote spelling words and high-frequency words to complete sentences. Have your child identify and spell the five list words that are most difficult for him or her.

Name _____

More About Pronouns

Imagine you are using a machine.
Write about what happens.
Use the pronouns **it**, **he**, **him**, **she**, **her**,
I, **me**, **we**, or **us**.

_____
- -
_____

_____
- -
_____

_____
- -
_____

_____
- -
_____

_____
- -
_____

Home Activity Your child learned how to use pronouns in writing. Take turns with your child writing sentences using the pronouns listed on this page.

1.20.A.6 Understand and use pronouns in the context of reading, writing, and speaking.

Name _____

Words with *oi, oy*

Write these words in ABC order.

soil
voice
point
toy

1. _____

2. _____

3. _____

4. _____

Use this code. **Write** the words.

5. _____

6. _____

7. _____

8. _____

9. _____

10. _____

School + Home

Home Activity Your child has been learning to spell words with the vowel sound in *boy* spelled *oi* and *oy*. Help your child brainstorm other words with *oi* and *oy*.

1.22.A.1 Use phonological knowledge to match sounds to letters to construct words.

More About Pronouns

Mark the pronoun that can replace the underlined word or words.

1. <u>The young girl</u> has many ideas.
   - ○ She
   - ○ Them
   - ○ We

2. Her mother asks <u>Sara</u> about her plan.
   - ○ he
   - ○ she
   - ○ her

3. Sara sees <u>a big mess</u>.
   - ○ her
   - ○ it
   - ○ you

4. <u>Sara's friends</u> help her clean.
   - ○ Them
   - ○ He
   - ○ They

5. Her plan surprises <u>the neighbors</u>.
   - ○ them
   - ○ they
   - ○ we

Home Activity Your child prepared for taking tests on pronouns. Read aloud a favorite storybook to your child. Ask your child to say "Stop" each time he or she hears a pronoun and to identify the pronoun.

1.20.A.6 Understand and use pronouns in the context of reading, writing, and speaking.

Name _____

Circle the word for each picture.

 saw   **au**to

1.	2.	3.	4.
pail paw	yawn yard	lunch launch	stray straw

5.	6.	7.	8.
false faucet	crawl call	lane lawn	laundry landed

Pick a word to finish each sentence. **Circle** the word.
Write the word in the sentence.

9. I like pasta with _____ .

       sauce   sash

10. The bear used his _____ to open the bag.

       clay   claw

 School + Home   **Home Activity** Your child read words with the vowel sounds *aw* and *au* as heard in *saw* and *auto*. Have your child make silly rhyming sentences using words that rhyme with *saw*. Example: *The cat can draw with her paw*.

1.3.A.1.v.11 Decode words in context by applying common letter-sound correspondences, including: vowel digraphs including *aw*. **Also 1.3.A.2.v.11, 1.3.A.1.v.12, 1.3.A.2.v.12.**

Name _____

Read the sentence.
Unscramble the letters.
Write the word on the line.

| built   early   learn   science   through |

_____
- -
1. Many boys and girls like **sciceen**. _____

_____
- -
2. We **lnear** about plants. _____

_____

3. We get up **earyl** to see the
- -

sun rise. _____

_____
- -
4. We **uiltb** a little car! _____

_____
- -
5. We look **ourghth** the glass. _____

Home Activity Your child learned to identify and read the words *built*, *early*, *learn*, *science*, and *through*. Find children's books about famous scientists and mathematicians. Read them together and challenge your child to find the words in the text.

1.3.H.1 Identify at least 100 high-frequency words from a commonly used list. **Also 1.3.H.2.**

© Pearson Education. Inc. 1

Name _____

Read the story. **Follow** the directions.

Mr. Lee's class is going on a trip. First they all get on the bus. It is going to be a fun day. Then the class gets off the bus at Rock Park Zoo. Rock Park Zoo is a big zoo. Next the class walks to the snake house.

1. **Circle** words in the story that help you know the order of events.

2. **Write 1, 2, 3** to show the order of story events.

                                                         _____

The class gets on the bus.   _____

The class walks to the snake house.   _____

The class gets off the bus   _____

3. **Draw** a picture of what might happen next. Then **retell** the story in correct order.

School + Home **Home Activity** Your child identified order words and used them to put story events in the correct order. Have your child use order words to tell you what he or she does in the morning.

1.14.C.1 Retell the order of events in a text by referring to words.
Also 1.14.C.2, RC-1.E.1.

Comprehension Sequence   **571**

Name _____

Writing Prompt: Think about something great that happened to you. Now write an autobiography that tells about it.

 The Best Day

   Last year I was with Mom in a store. A lady asked me to be in a TV ad for the store. I happily said yes. The next day, Mom took me to the store. The lady was there. She told me what to do. She said I should act normally. We practiced for the ad. Then we quickly taped it. The ad was on TV! Soon my family and friends saw it.

🌐 **1.18.A** Write brief stories that include a beginning, middle, and end.

Name _____

Circle the word that names each picture.

1.

platter   painter   painting

2.

toyshop   trays   toolbox

3.

nose   nothing   noisemaker

4.

another   awning   author

Write the word from the box to finish each sentence.

oatmeal   endpoint   football   boyhood

5. A bowl of hot _____ is good for you.

6. I like to play _____.

7. He had a great _____.

8. A dot at the end of a line is an _____.

School + Home

Home Activity Your child read compound words with vowel diphthongs (*oi*, *oy*) and vowel digraphs (*oa*). Have your child read the following words aloud and then make up a sentence for each: *football*, *boyhood*, and *oatmeal*.

1.3.C.1.v Use common syllabication patterns to decode words, including vowel digraphs and diphthongs.

Name _____

Words with *aw*

Write a list word that belongs in the group.

1. jay, eagle, _____

2. hammer, sandpaper, _____

3. skull, ribs, _____

4. skip, walk, _____

5. paint, sketch, _____

6. rule, order, _____

Write the missing word.

7. I sat on the _____ .

8. My dog sat on some _____ .

9. He put his _____ on my leg.

10. We both began to _____ .

Home Activity Your child spelled words with the vowel sound in *saw*. Have your child name the two letters common to all the spelling words (*aw*).

1.22.A.1 Use phonological knowledge to match sounds to letters to construct words.

Adverbs

I learned a song **today**.
Today tells when.

Aleck worked on his invention **downstairs**.
Downstairs tells where.

Circle the adverb in each sentence that tells when or where.
Say a new sentence for each adverb.

1. Aleck got sick often.

2. Aleck went away to get better.

3. I built my invention yesterday.

4. I thought a lot about it before.

5. I got a good idea recently.

6. I will work on it next.

Home Activity Your child learned about adverbs that tell when and where. With your child, make a list of all the adverbs you can think of that tell when and where.

1.20.A.4 Understand and use adverbs about time in the context of reading, writing, and speaking.

Conventions Adverbs **575**

Autobiography
Top-Score Response

Focus/Ideas	A good autobiography tells about real events in the author's life.
Organization	A good autobiography is told in time order.
Voice	A good autobiography tells how the author feels about the events.
Word Choice	A good autobiography uses words that tell how, when, or where events happened.
Sentences	A good autobiography uses sentences that work together to tell the writer's ideas.
Conventions	A good autobiography uses words like **I** and **me**.

Home Activity Your child is learning how writers tell events in their own lives. Have your child tell you about an event from his or her life.

1.17 Use elements of the writing process to compose text.
1.17.B Develop drafts by sequencing ideas through writing sentences.

Name _____

Copy the **sentences**. Leave the correct space between words.

1. Laura has a new shawl.

2. We saw the vault.

3. Maureen made sauce.

4. I saw a drawing.

5. The baby can crawl.

Did you leave the correct space between your words? | Yes | No |

Home Activity Your child practiced writing sentences with words with *aw* and *au*. Have your child choose one sentence to copy on a separate sheet of paper.

1.21.A.1 Form upper-case letters legibly in text, using the basic conventions of print (left-to-right and top-to-bottom progression), including spacing between words and sentences. **Also 1.21.A.2.**

Name _____

Look at the Web page.
Answer the questions.

Click on a picture to learn more.

car   television   oven

1. Which button would you click on to look at the page you

_____

- -

looked at before this one? _____

2. Which picture would you click on to make a paper copy of the

_____

- -

information on this page? _____

3. What is the address of this page?

_____

- -

_____

- -

4. What is the title of this page? _____

5. What would you do to learn more about ovens?

_____

- -

Home Activity Your child learned about using a Web page to find information. When you and your child are online, discuss how to navigate the Web.

⊕ **1.23.B.1** Decide what sources of information might be relevant to answer these questions. **Also 1.24.A.1.**

Paul Bunyan

Vowel Sound *aw, au*	Syllable Patterns: Digraphs and Diphthongs		High Frequency Words	
Paul	boyhood	sailboats	a	of
yawned	football	oatmeal	was	other
dawn		seacoast	as	do
sawed			the	
Paul's				
straw				

People tell tall tales about Paul Bunyan.

Paul had quite a boyhood.

His room was as big as ten football fields.

Paul had a blue ox named Babe.

Babe ate thirty bales of straw for a snack.

What other tall tales do people tell?

Decodable Story *Paul Bunyan*
Target Skills Vowel Sound *aw, au*; Syllable Patterns: Digraphs and Diphthongs

🌐 **1.3.A.2.v.11** Decode words in isolation by applying common letter-sound correspondences, including: vowel digraphs including *aw*. **Also 1.3.A.1.v.11, 1.3.A.1.v.12, 1.3.C.1.v, 1.3.A.2.v12, 1.3.F.2.**

Paul liked to look at the seacoast.

When Paul yawned, he slurped the sailboats right out of the sea.

Paul ate nine bathtubs of oatmeal each dawn.

Then Paul and his dad sawed wood.

Paul was a hard worker.

Words with *aw*

Spelling Words				
saw	draw	crawl	straw	law
jaw	paw	lawn	yawn	hawk

High-Frequency Words
science
through

Write the missing list word.

1. The _____ says to wear seatbelts.

2. The baby is learning to _____.

3. Did you mow the _____?

4. Look at that _____ fly.

5. My _____ is sore.

6. Let's _____ a picture.

7. We _____ a snake.

8. My cat has one white _____.

9. Sue drank _____ a straw.

10. I like to study _____.

Home Activity Your child wrote spelling words and high-frequency words to complete sentences. Help your child make silly sentences by substituting other list words in the sentences. For example: The **hawk** says to wear seatbelts.

1.22.A.1 Use phonological knowledge to match sounds to letters to construct words. **1.22.C.1** Spell high-frequency words from a commonly used list.

Name _____

Adverbs

Write about a time you built or made something.
Use **adverbs** to tell when and where.
Read your story aloud to the class.

_____
- -
_____
- -
_____
- -
_____
- -
_____
- -
_____
- -
_____
- -
_____

Choose other adverbs. **Say** a sentence for each adverb.

Home Activity Your child learned how to use adverbs in writing. Have your child read aloud the story he or she wrote on this page. Ask your child to point out the adverbs.

1.20.A.4 Understand and use adverbs about time in the context of reading, writing, and speaking.

Name _____

Words with *aw*

Spelling Words

| saw | draw | crawl | straw | law |
| jaw | paw | lawn | yawn | hawk |

Draw lines through all the **p**'s and **o**'s.
Write the word that is left.

1. h o a p w p k o

1. _____

2. l o o a p w p n

2. _____

3. p c o r p a w p l

3. _____

4. y o a p w p p n o

4. _____

Write six list words that rhyme with **thaw**.

5. _____   6. _____

7. _____   8. _____

9. _____   10. _____

School + Home

Home Activity Your child has been learning to spell words with the vowel sound in *saw*. Help your child use the list words to make more word puzzles similar to those at the top of this page.

1.22.A.1 Use phonological knowledge to match sounds to letters to construct words.

Spelling Words with *aw*   583

Adverbs

Fill in the circle by the adverb that tells when or where.

1. Maya and I built our invention yesterday.
   - ○ Maya
   - ○ built
   - ○ yesterday

2. We made it upstairs in my room.
   - ○ We
   - ○ upstairs
   - ○ my

3. We had to start over often.
   - ○ had
   - ○ start
   - ○ often

4. Soon, we figured it out.
   - ○ Soon
   - ○ figured
   - ○ out

5. Next, we showed our parents.
   - ○ Next
   - ○ we
   - ○ parents

Home Activity Your child prepared for taking tests on adverbs that tell when and where. Read aloud a favorite story to your child. Have your child listen for adverbs that tell when and where.

1.20.A.4 Understand and use adverbs about time in the context of reading, writing, and speaking.

Name _____

Add re- or **un-** to the word in ( ).
Write the new word on the line.

re- + do = <u>re</u>do
un- + clear = <u>un</u>clear

(build)

_____

----

1. Mr. Ford will _____ the car.

(happy)

_____

----

2. He is _____ with the color.

(paint)

_____

----

3. He will _____ it.

(fills)

_____

----

4. He _____ the car with gas.

(lock)

_____

----

5. Don't forget to _____ the door!

School + Home

Home Activity Your child added the prefixes *un-* and *re-* to words. Ask your child to think of other words to which *un-* and *re-* can be added. Have him or her list the words and use them in sentences.

1.3.C Use common syllabicaton patterns to decode words. **Also** 1.3.D.

Name _____

Pick a word from the box to finish each sentence.
Write it on the line.

poor   answered
different   carry

1. The soil was so _____ that nothing grew.

2. I _____ all the questions about my garden.

3. All of the flowers were _____ colors.

4. I have to _____ the garden tools to the backyard.

Pick two words from the box.
Write your own sentences using each word.

5. _____

_____

6. _____

_____

7. _____

_____

8. _____

Home Activity Your child learned to read and identify the words *answered, carry, different,* and *poor*. Encourage your child to make up a story that uses these words and draw pictures to illustrate the story.

1.3.H.1 Identify at least 100 high-frequency words from a commonly used list. **Also 1.3.H.2.**

Name _____

Read the story. **Answer** the questions.

This story is a folktale. It was passed along by the native people in the Philippines.

The Stars and the Moon

Long ago, the sky was close to the ground. A woman wanted to pound rice with her hammer. Before she started, she took off her beads from her neck. She took off the comb in her hair. She hung them both on the sky. Each time she raised her hammer, it would hit the sky. One time her hammer struck the sky so hard that the sky began to rise. It went up so far she lost her beads and comb. They never came back. The comb became the moon. The beads became the stars.

---

1. What is the big idea of the story?

_____
_____
_____

2. How did the woman change the sky and the ground?

_____
_____
_____

3. How do you know this is a folktale?

_____
_____
_____

Home Activity Your child has learned about themes in stories. As you read stories with your child, discuss the big ideas in the stories.

1.7 Analyze, make inferences, and draw conclusions about theme.

Comprehension Theme **587**

Name _____

Writing · Poem

 My Piggy Bank

"Milk's all gone,"

said my older brother Sean.

He threw the jug in the trash can,

but I took it out and ran

right to the sink to wash it clean.

Then I used a marker to paint it green.

Now the jug's my very own piggy bank.

For that I have my brother Sean to thank.

Key Features of a Poem

· Many poems are shorter than a story.

· The lines in a poem often end with rhyming words.

1.18.B.1 Write short poems that convey sensory details.

Name _____

Circle the word for each picture.

p<u>ost</u>   g<u>old</u>   r<u>ind</u>   w<u>ild</u>

1.   fold   fell

2.   kite   kind

3.   child   chilled

4.   mast   most

5.   cold   call

6.   fin   find

7.   wind   went

8.   old   all

Circle the word to finish each sentence.

9. I told / tied my baby sister a story.

10. I can't fine / find my pencil.

School + Home

Home Activity Your child read words with the long *o* sound as in *post* and *gold* and the long *i* sound as in *rind* and *wild*. Use each word in a sentence with your child.

1.3.A.ii Decode words in context and in isolation by applying common letter-sound correspondences.

Phonics Long Vowels *o, i*   **589**

Name _____

Words with Prefixes *un-, re-*

Spelling Words				
unhappy	refill	untie	undo	repay
unkind	undress	retell	reopen	rewind

Circle a word to finish the sentence. **Write** it.

_____

1. Will you   **unkind**   **untie**   my ribbon?   _____

2. She looks   **unhappy**   **repay** .   _____

3. Please   **refill**   **reopen**   the book.   _____

4. She will   **repay**   **unhappy**   you.   _____

5. Please   **retell**   **undress**   that story.   _____

6. I will   **retell**   **undress**   the doll.   _____

7. Please   **rewind**   **undo**   the movie.   _____

8. Can you   **repay**   **undo**   this knot?   _____

9. He is   **rewind**   **unkind**   to the dog.   _____

10. He will   **retell**   **refill**   the glasses.   _____

Home Activity Your child spelled words to complete sentences. Read a sentence on this page. Ask your child to identify the word with the prefix *re-* or *un-* and spell it.

1.22.A.1 Use phonological knowledge to match sounds to letters to construct words.

Prepositions and Prepositional Phrases

A **preposition** is the first word in a group of words called a **prepositional phrase.**

Preposition	Momoko sat <u>on</u> the steps.
Prepositional Phrase	Momoko sat <u>on the steps.</u>

Circle the preposition in each sentence.
Say a new sentence using each preposition.

I. Susie read a book about gardens.

2. Susie wanted a garden in her yard.

3. She started working before school.

4. She planted flowers after school.

Write the prepositional phrase in the sentence.
Say other prepositional phrases that could replace it.

5. I got a good idea in the morning.

_____

- -

_____

 Home Activity Your child learned about prepositions. Read an article to your child. Have him or her identify prepositional phrases from the article.

1.20.A.5 Understand and use prepositions and prepositional phrases in the context of reading, writing, and speaking.

Name _____

Sequence

First

Next

Last

Home Activity Your child has planned a poem. Play a word game by making up phrases that rhyme with household words, such as *bed* (sleepy head) or *book* (take a look).

⊕ **1.17.A** Plan a first draft by generating ideas for writing.

Name _____

Copy the **sentences.** Leave the correct space between words.

1. Please unfold the paper.

_____

_____

2. He will unlock the safe.

_____

_____

3. The store will reopen.

_____

_____

4. Rewrite your name.

_____

_____

5. Let's unload the box.

_____

_____

Did you leave the correct space between your words? | Yes | | No |

Home Activity Your child practiced writing sentences using words that begin with *un-* and *re-*. Write the following words on a sheet of paper and have your child read and rewrite them as neatly as possible: *rejoin, remake, unseen, unkind.*

1.21.A.1 Form upper-case letters legibly in text, using the basic conventions of print (left-to-right and top-to-bottom progression), including spacing between words and sentences. **Also 1.21.A.2.**

Name _____

Look at the picture.
Read the introduction.
Write what each character will say.
Present the play.

One day, a boy walked into town. He was hungry.
He had a pot and a stone. He decided to make stone soup.

Stone Soup: The Play

Boy: I am going to make stone soup, but I need vegetables.

_____

Farmer: _____

Woman: Here are some onions.

Young Girl: Here are some tomatoes.

_____

Young Boy: _____

Mule: Here is some water.

Boy: The soup is ready. Please have some.

Everyone: By working together, everyone enjoyed the soup.

Home Activity Your child learned how to write a script. Together with your child, think of a favorite folktale, fairy tale, or other story that you enjoy. Work together to write a script based on the characters of the story. If possible, cast the characters and present the play as a family.

🌐 **1.26.A.2** Create a visual display (with adult assistance) to convey the results of the research. **Also 1.26.A.2.**

Quincy's Bad Day

Prefixes un- and re-	Long o and Long i		High-Frequency Words	
unhappy	told	wild	you	the
unlocked	sold	kind	I	to
unwise	old	find	said	your
replace	folded		a	some
restart	most			

"You look most unhappy," Jess told Quincy.

"I AM unhappy," Quincy said.

"Why?" asked Jess with a kind smile.

Jess folded her arms.

"It's unwise to stay sad," she said. "Let's restart your day and have some fun!"

Decodable Story *Quincy's Bad Day*
Target Skills Prefixes *un-* and *re-*; Long *o* and Long *i*

🕮 **1.3.C** Use common syllabication patterns to decode words. **Also 1.3.A.ii, 1.3.D.**

"First, Dad sold my old bike.
"I hope I can replace it."

"Then, the dog went wild.

He ran out the unlocked gate.

I didn't find him until just now."

Name _____

Words with Prefixes *un-*, *re-*

Spelling Words					High-Frequency Words
unhappy	refill	untie	undo	repay	different
unkind	undress	retell	reopen	rewind	through

Write the prefix **un-** or **re-**. **Write** the list word.

1. Dad will _____tell the joke.

2. I can _____tie my shoes.

3. Let's _____do this puzzle.

4. He was _____kind to Sam.

5. She is _____happy.

6. You must _____pay the loan.

7. The men will _____open the crate.

8. Can you _____wind the tape?

Write the word that has the same meaning.

9. not alike _____   10. into _____

Home Activity Your child wrote words with the prefixes *un-* and *re-*. Have your child name the base word in each list word and tell how adding the prefix changes the meaning.

★ **1.22.A.1** Use phonological knowledge to match sounds to letters to construct words. **1.22.C.1** Spell high-frequency words from a commonly used list.

Spelling Words with Prefixes *un-*, *re-*   **597**

Prepositions and Prepositional Phrases

Imagine you are helping build a garden.

Write about what happens. **Use** prepositional phrases.

_____

- -

_____

- -

_____

- -

_____

- -

_____

- -

_____

Choose other prepositions. **Say** a sentence for each preposition.

Home Activity Your child learned how to use prepositions in writing. Take turns with your child writing sentences using prepositional phrases.

1.20.A.5 Understand and use prepositions and prepositional phrases in the context of reading, writing, and speaking.

Words with Prefixes *un-, re-*

Spelling Words				
unhappy	refill	untie	undo	repay
unkind	undress	retell	reopen	rewind

Read the words in the box.
Add un- or **re-** to make a list word. **Write** it.

pay	tell
wind	fill

1. _____   2. _____

3. _____   4. _____

Find a list word in each row of letters. **Circle** it. **Write** it.

5. **r u n t i e s t**   5. _____

6. **t h r e o p e n**   6. _____

7. **u n k i n d e s**   7. _____

8. **x u n d r e s s**   8. _____

9. **w i u n d o t s**   9. _____

10. **s u n h a p p y**   10. _____

Home Activity Your child has been learning to spell words with the prefixes *un-* and *re-*. Help your child think of other words with these prefixes.

1.22.A.1 Use phonological knowledge to match sounds to letters to construct words.

Spelling Words with Prefixes *un-, re-*   **599**

Prepositions and Prepositional Phrases

Mark the word in each sentence that is a preposition.

1. The yard was bordered with homes like hers.
   - ○ The
   - ○ yard
   - ○ with

2. Except for old tires, the yard was cold and bare.
   - ○ Except
   - ○ tires
   - ○ the

3. The neighbors watched Momoko from their windows.
   - ○ neighbors
   - ○ from
   - ○ windows

4. Momoko planted the bulbs across the yard.
   - ○ Momoko
   - ○ bulbs
   - ○ across

5. People would sit and visit in the evenings.
   - ○ People
   - ○ sit
   - ○ in

Home Activity Your child prepared for taking tests on prepositions. Read aloud a favorite story to your child. Have your child say "Stop" each time he or she hears a prepositional phrase.

600 **Conventions** Prepositions and Prepositional Phrases

1.20.A.5 Understand and use prepositions and prepositional phrases in the context of reading, writing, and speaking.

Writing Process Lessons

Name _____

Story Chart

Fill out this story chart to help you organize your ideas. Write your ideas in sentences.

_____

Title _____

Beginning

Middle

End

🌐 **1.17.A.1** Plan a first draft by generating ideas for writing.
1.17.B.1 Develop drafts by sequencing ideas through writing sentences.

Unit 1 Writing Process   **603**

Name _____

Use Words That Tell How You Feel

Write a word from the box to tell how the writer feels.

Use each word one time. The pictures will help you.

Word Bank
happy
sad
scared
mad

1. My brother took my book.

   _____

   I feel _____ .

2. I won a prize.

   _____

   I feel _____ .

3. My best friend moved away.

   _____

   I feel _____ .

4. A dog growled at me.

   _____

   I feel _____ .

★ Develop drafts by using words that tell about feelings.

Adding a Word, Phrase, or Sentence

Read each set of sentences. **Answer** the question.

1. What word did the writer add? Write the word.

   I saw a fish.

   I saw a huge fish.

   _____

   -

   _____

2. What phrase did the writer add? Write the phrase.

   The fish swam.

   The fish swam into me.

   _____

   -

   _____

3. What sentence did the writer add? Write the sentence.

   Then the fish swam away.

   Then the fish swam away. I laughed.

   _____

   -

   _____

1.17.C.1 Revise drafts by adding a word, phrase, or sentence.

Unit 1 Writing Process   **605**

Name _____

Self-Evaluation Guide

Check *Yes* or *No* about voice in your story.

	Yes	No
I. I used words that tell feelings or opinions.		
2. I used one or more words that describe.		
3. I used one or more words that show action.		

Answer the questions.

4. What is the best part of your story?

_____

_____

_____

_____

5. What is one thing you would change about this story if you could write it again?

_____

_____

_____

_____

★ Evaluate the final writing product.

Name _____

Letter Chart

Fill out this letter chart to help you organize your ideas.
Write your ideas in sentences.

Whom is the letter for?

What is the main idea of the letter?

What details support the main idea?

Whom is the letter from?

1.17.A.1 Plan a first draft by generating ideas for writing.
1.17.B.1 Develop drafts by sequencing ideas through writing sentences.

Unit 2 Writing Process   **607**

Name _____

Use Correct Letter Form

Write the date, greeting, and closing from the box to complete the letter. **Put** commas in the correct places. **Write** your name at the end.

> Yours truly
> May 4 2011
> Dear Ms. Allen

_____

_____

_____

You are a good worker. You are always there.

You make sure kids get to school safely.

Thank you.

_____

_____

_____

_____

1.19.B.3 Write short letters that use appropriate conventions.

Name _____

Deleting a Word, Phrase, or Sentence

Read the sentences. **Follow** the directions.

1. The fire alarm was so so loud!

   Delete, or take out, the word that is not needed. Write the sentence.

   _____
   -
   _____
   -
   _____

2. Juan was scared and afraid.

   Delete the phrase that is not needed. Write the sentence.

   _____
   -
   _____
   -
   _____

3. Juan found out there was no fire. The firefighter said there was no fire.

   Delete one sentence that is not needed. Write the other sentence.

   _____
   -
   _____
   -
   _____

1.17.C.2 Revise drafts by deleting a word, phrase, or sentence.

Name _____

Editing 1

Edit these sentences. **Look** for errors in grammar, punctuation, capitalization, and spelling. **Use** proofreading marks to show the corrections.

Proofreading Marks	
Delete (Take out)	ꝺ
Add	^
Spelling	⬭
Uppercase letter	≡
Lowercase letter	/

1. The girls cros the street.

2. They need help

3. Mr. james helps them.

4. The girls is happy.

5. We hav many helpers.

Now you will edit the draft of your letter. Use the rubric from your teacher to check the grammar, punctuation, and spelling in your letter. Then, use your draft to make a final copy of your letter. Finally, you will publish your writing and share it with others.

🌐 **1.17.D** Edit drafts for grammar, punctuation, and spelling using a teacher-developed rubric. **1.17.E** Publish and share writing with others.

Name _____

Main Idea and Details Chart

Fill in the chart with the main idea and details for your expository article. **Write** your ideas in sentences.

```
┌─────────────────────────────────────────┐
│ Main Idea                                 │
│                                           │
│                                           │
│                                           │
│                                           │
└─────────────────────────────────────────┘

┌─────────────────────────────────────────┐
│ Detail                                    │
│                                           │
│                                           │
│                                           │
│                                           │
└─────────────────────────────────────────┘

┌─────────────────────────────────────────┐
│ Detail                                    │
│                                           │
│                                           │
│                                           │
│                                           │
└─────────────────────────────────────────┘

┌─────────────────────────────────────────┐
│ Detail                                    │
│                                           │
│                                           │
│                                           │
│                                           │
└─────────────────────────────────────────┘
```

1.17.A.1 Plan a first draft by generating ideas for writing.
1.17.B.1 Develop drafts by sequencing ideas through writing sentences.

Unit 3 Writing Process 611

Name _____

Strong Verbs

Add a strong verb from the box to each sentence.

> buzzes   gleams
> bends   paddles   splashes

1. The lake _____ in the sun.

2. A duck _____ to shore.

3. Water _____ on the rocks.

4. The grass _____ in the wind.

5. A bee _____ by my ear.

🌐 **1.20.A.1.ii** Understand and use verbs (present) in the context of reading, writing, and speaking. ★ Develop drafts by using strong verbs.

Name _____

Adding or Deleting a Phrase or Sentence

Read the sentence. **Follow** the directions.

1. The birds fly.

   Add a phrase to the sentence. Tell where the birds fly.
   Write the new sentence.

   _____
   -
   _____

2. The birds eat grass.

   Add a sentence. Tell why the birds eat grass. Write the new
   sentence.

   _____
   -
   _____

3. The autumn leaves are red in the fall.

   Delete the phrase that is not needed. Write the new sentence.

   _____
   -
   _____

4. There are a lot of trees in the woods. The forest has many
   trees. Some are tall, and some are short.

   Delete a sentence that is not needed. Write the other
   sentences.

   _____
   -
   _____
   -
   _____

Name _____

Editing 2

Edit these sentences. **Look** for errors in grammar, punctuation, capitalization, and spelling. **Use** proofreading marks to show the corrections.

Proofreading Marks	
Delete (Take out)	ℨ
Add	^
Spelling	◯
Uppercase letter	≡
Lowercase letter	/

1. The beach has big wavs.

2. It is named for a man, will rogers.

3. Is there shells in the sand?

4. The water feels very cold

5. The air smels like salt.

Now you will edit the draft of your expository article. Use the rubric from your teacher to check the grammar, punctuation, and spelling in your expository article. Then, use your draft to make a final copy of your expository article. Finally, you will publish your writing and share it with others.

1.17.D Edit drafts for grammar, punctuation, and spelling using a teacher-developed rubric. **1.17.E** Publish and share writing with others.

Name _____

Story Chart

Fill in this story chart to help you organize your ideas.
Write your ideas in sentences.

Title _____

```
┌─────────────────────────────────────┐
│ Beginning                            │
│                                      │
│                                      │
│                                      │
└─────────────────────────────────────┘
               ↓
┌─────────────────────────────────────┐
│ Middle                               │
│                                      │
│                                      │
│                                      │
└─────────────────────────────────────┘
               ↓
┌─────────────────────────────────────┐
│ End                                  │
│                                      │
│                                      │
│                                      │
└─────────────────────────────────────┘
```

© Pearson Education, Inc., 1

1.17.A.1 Plan a first draft by generating ideas for writing.
1.17.B.1 Develop drafts by sequencing ideas through writing sentences.

Good Adjectives

Add an adjective from the box to each sentence.

> loud   five
> tall   sunny   wild

1. It was a _____ spring day.

2. Maria heard _____ quacks.

3. The _____ ducks had a nest.

4. It was in the _____ grass.

5. Maria saw _____ baby ducks.

1.20.A.3 Understand and use descriptive adjectives in the context of reading, writing, and speaking. ★ Develop drafts by using good adjectives.

Name _____

Adding or Deleting a Word or Phrase

Read the sentence. **Follow** the directions.

1. Tim walked.

Add a phrase to the sentence. Tell where Tim walked. Write the new sentence.

_____

- - - - - - - - - - - - - - - -

_____

- - - - - - - - - - - - - - - -

_____

2. Tim got a game.

Add a word to the sentence. Tell more about the game. Write the new sentence.

- - - - - - - - - - - - - - - -

_____

- - - - - - - - - - - - - - - -

_____

3. Tim and Juan had fun with the fun game.

Delete a word that is not needed. Draw a line through the word.

4. Tom left his game and forgot it at Juan's house.

Delete a phrase that is not needed. Draw a line through the phrase.

1.17.C.1 Revise drafts by adding a word, phrase, or sentence.
1.17.C.2 Revise drafts by deleting a word, phrase, or sentence.

Unit 4 Writing Process **617**

© Pearson Education, Inc., 1

Name _____

Editing 3

Proofreading Marks	
Delete (Take out)	ꝺ
Add	^
Spelling	⬭
Uppercase letter	≡
Lowercase letter	/

This is part of a realistic story. **Edit** this paragraph. **Look** for errors in grammar, punctuation, capitalization, and spelling. **Use** proofreading marks to show the corrections.

Lee loved too read. Her favorite book was about a girl and her dog. Lee readed it every night. One day the book was lost. Lee looked all over that night she was sad. She could not read her favorite book. She could not slep. Her pillow felt hard. She look under it. There was her book! Lee was so gladd.

Now you will edit the draft of your realistic story. Use the rubric from your teacher to check the grammar, punctuation, and spelling in your realistic story. Then, use your draft to make a final copy of your realistic story. Finally, you will publish your writing and share it with others.

Writing Process Unit 4

618 Unit 4 Writing Process

1.17.D Edit drafts for grammar, punctuation, and spelling using a teacher-developed rubric. **1.17.E** Publish and share writing with others.

Name _____

K-W-L Chart

Fill out this K-W-L chart to help you organize your ideas. **Write** your ideas in sentences.

What We Know	What We Want to Know	What We Learned

⊕ **1.17.A.1** Plan a first draft by generating ideas for writing.
1.17.B.1 Develop drafts by sequencing ideas through writing sentences.

Unit 5 Writing Process 619

Name _____

Writing Trait: Sentences

• Use all kinds of sentences: statements, questions, commands, and exclamations.

• Use different beginnings. Don't start too many sentences with **the, he,** or **she.**

Write the letter of each sentence next to the word that identifies what kind of sentence it is.

(A) Who is Alexander Graham Bell? **(B)** He invented the telephone. **(C)** That's a wonderful invention! **(D)** Don't forget about his work with deaf people.

1. Statement: _____   3. Command: _____

2. Question: _____   4. Exclamation: _____

Rearrange the words in each sentence so it begins with the underlined word. **Write** the paragraph.

Example: She invented a new game <u>last week</u>.

Answer: Last week she invented a new game.

She played the game <u>today</u>. She changed it <u>later</u>. She likes it better <u>now</u>!

_____

_____

_____

_____

★ Develop drafts by varying sentence kinds and structures.

Name _____

Adding or Deleting a Word or Sentence

Read the sentence. **Follow** the directions.

1. Kate invented a toy.

   Add a word to describe the toy. Write the new sentence.

   _____

   _____

   _____

2. The toy can sing.

   Add a sentence. Tell what else the toy can do. Write both sentences.

   _____

   _____

   _____

3. The first kite was a huge giant leaf.

   Delete a word that is not needed. Draw a line through the word.

4. The first Ferris wheel was 250 feet tall. How tall is the Statue of Liberty? Many people could ride on the Ferris wheel.

   Delete the sentence that does not belong. Draw a line through the sentence.

1.17.C.1 Revise drafts by adding a word, phrase, or sentence. **1.17.C.2** Revise drafts by deleting a word, phrase, or sentence.

Unit 5 Writing Process   **621**

Self-Evaluation Guide

Check **Yes** or **No** about sentences in your report.

	Yes	No
1. I used facts in my research report.		
2. I used different kinds of sentences.		
3. I used different beginnings for my sentences.		

Answer the questions.

4. What is the best part of your report?

_____

_____

_____

_____

5. What is one thing you would change about this report if you
   could write it again?

_____

_____

_____

_____

★ Evaluate the final writing product.

Name _____

My Rubric

Title _____

Features of the Writing	4	3	2	1
Content				
Grammar				
Punctuation				
Spelling				

To the Teacher
Use this information to help students use the rubric.
4 = The feature is fully developed in the writing.
3 = The feature is present in the writing, but is not
    fully developed.
2 = The feature is not clearly present in the writing
1 = The feature is not present in the writing.